Before We Go

Before We Go

*An Ongoing Philosophy of Lifting,
Living and Learning*

Dan John

Foreword
TC Luoma

Editor
Gregory R duManoir, PhD

On Target Publications
Santa Cruz, California

Before We Go
An Ongoing Philosophy of Lifting, Living and Learning

Dan John

Foreword by TC Luoma
Edited by Gregory R duManoir, PhD

Cover image by Chip Conrad

Articles originally published on *t-nation.com, menshealth.com, danjohn.net & bodybuilding.com*

ISBN-13: 978-1-931046-91-6
First printing January 2016

On Target Publications
PO Box 1335
Aptos, California 95001 USA
otpbooks.com

Library of Congress Cataloging-in-Publication Data
John, Dan.
  Before we go : an ongoing philosophy of lifting, living and learning
/ Dan John ; foreword, TC Luoma.
    p. cm.
  Includes index.
  ISBN 978-1-931046-91-6 (pbk.)
  1. Weight lifting. 2. Weight training. 3. Bodybuilding. 4. Physical
education and training.   I. Title.
  GV546.3.J64 2016
  613.7'1301—dc22
                    2016012888

Also by Dan John

Can You Go?

Intervention

Never Let Go

From Dad to Grad

Mass Made Simple

Easy Strength (co-writer)

Fat Loss Happens on Monday (co-writer)

To Dick and Joy Notmeyer

Forty years ago Dick allowed me to train at his gym five days
a week for twenty-five cents. During our daily three-hour
sessions, he taught me the Olympic lifts, nutrition and training.

But, more importantly, he taught me the Laws of Success.
He remains my foundation and my main mentor.
I dedicate this book…and my career…to him.

Contents

Contents

Foreword

AMBROSE BIERCE WAS A JOURNALIST and short story writer who terrorized famous or powerful people in the late 1800s and early 1900s. I say "terrorized" because the guy was a world-class SOB when he wanted to be. When Bierce zinged you, well, you might as well have pulled the flannel covers over your head and hoped he eventually forgot you, because there was no way any comeback you dreamed up would be half as witty or half as cutting.

And it didn't matter if you were dead, as he exhibited no sympathy or decorum for anyone simply because they'd had the understandable but futile instinct to escape his notice by dying. For instance, in reference to a deceased actress, Bierce wrote, "Always famous for her composed manner, she is now quite decomposed."

And once, when reviewing a book, he merely wrote, "The covers of this book are too far apart," which brings me to *this* book by Dan John.

The covers of this book are *also* too far apart.

But I don't mean it the same way Bierce did. This book just has *too much information in it;* that's why I think the covers are too far apart.

The book makes me itch. It gives me hives. I feel like I've stumbled onto some heavenly smorgasbord that features heaping amounts of all my favorite foods, and I just don't know where to start.

I feel like the Russian immigrant Robin Williams played in *Moscow on the Hudson,* who, in his first days in America, was tasked to go to the grocery store to buy some coffee. Used to waiting in long lines only to be handed a ration of weak, generic coffee, he's overwhelmed by what he sees on the shelves.

He starts muttering "coffee...coffee...coffee..." until he collapses in a heap, overwhelmed by the sheer magnitude of the choices in front of him.

Granted, I've read many of the pieces in this compilation before, but where reading one might be like a drop of cold water hitting your forehead, gently urging you to adopt the lessons and challenges described therein, being presented by so many pieces together like this is like being shot in the face with a fire hose. It's shocking. It's almost rude. And it's terribly persuasive.

Dan John is like the Knute Rockne, Vince Lombardi, Herb Brooks, and even Jimmy Dugan (minus the drinking, of course) of fitness, training and healthy lifestyle.

If you're like me, you'll read through these chapters, and you'll feel a growing compulsion to make your body better, to make *you* better, because there's no one in the fitness biz that has Dan John's breadth or quality of experience. He has tried everything, improved everything, and come to more training "eureka" moments than anyone alive.

You'll likely become obsessed with kettlebells, sleds, slosh pipes, front squats, farmer walks, building more mass, losing bodyfat, getting stronger, feeling athletic, developing mobility, and doing correctives, and you'll want to have it all, and you'll want to do it all *today!*

So yeah, the covers of this book are too far apart.

But luckily, Dan has some reassuring words for me, and people like me, in the opening pages:

> *"Not every good idea, training device or diet should be done at once."*

And that's exactly what I've had to repeat to myself, over and over, while absorbing this book. So I go through one chapter at a time, slowly, and let it percolate.

I test drive the things suggested or the advice given and work them into my exercise program, my lifestyle, and my consciousness. If what's presented in a particular chapter doesn't match my current goals, I dog-ear the page and promise to come back to it when my goals do match it.

So I've made peace with this book and its far-apart covers. My body, I'm sure, will thank me for it.

TC Luoma
Editor-in-Chief, *T Nation*

Introduction

COMPILATIONS ALWAYS MAKE FOR A difficult introduction. Whereas Doctor Watson could always talk with Sherlock Holmes about the recent weather or cases too sensitive to discuss, the introduction here needs to remind the reader that the material contained within this book comes from blog posts and articles from all over the internet.

For someone who loves strength and conditioning, this formula has worked in the past. I never fly without a copy of John McCallum's classic work, *The Keys to Progress*, and, like all compilations, the material repeats itself, conflicts with itself and repeats itself (did I say that?). Another favorite, *Powerlifting Basics, Texas-Style: The Adventures of Lope Delk* by Paul Kelso, is as much fun today as the first time I read it in 1996. Annually, I reread both and still laugh at the gym antics, the protein tablets and the training mistake stories that have been with me most of my life.

Yet in both cases, the materials conflict and repeat themselves. My motto as an administrator was "Repetition Is the Mother of Implementation," so perhaps one should consider the repetitive points to be illuminating rather than annoying.

This is my second attempt at a compilation. No one was more surprised than me at the success of the first one, *Never Let Go*.

Originally, we planned a vanity publishing of perhaps 500 copies. In a three-day period a few years ago, Kindle readers downloaded 17,000 copies of the electronic version, and the book sells more every year since its first publication in 2009.

My other works, especially *Intervention* and *Can You Go?* provide the systematic approach I use for training both elite athletes and humanity in general. The process is fairly linear from the particular goal to the knowledge base and equipment available. From there, we just fill in the appropriate steps and put our energy into showing up and finishing the process.

I love systematic approaches to things. It's the basis of both geometry and theology where one's givens establish so much of the process of getting to the next step in the process, the "to prove."

In sports, the givens are often genetics and geography as where you were born and what tools you received at birth often influence the completion of the goal as much as expert coaching.

This book, like *Never Let Go*, is systemic education. Systemic education is how one generally learns religion, joins an elite cadre or cheers for a team. You don't join the Marine Corps by filling out some forms and taking an online exam. You have to go to boot camp and be dipped in the waters of being a Marine. It's the ultimate in learn-by-doing.

There's a time and place for step-by-step instruction. There's also a time to find out if the water is cold by jumping in. Right or wrong, in strength and conditioning I've been jumping in with both feet since 1965. And, I'm wrong a lot.

As I review the suggestions, the ideas and the material in this book, I can see the story behind so many of the insights. I learned hard lessons—some have ended in surgeries that have required up to two years of rehab—so, ideally, the reader doesn't have to repeat all my mistakes.

Please…please!…feel free to make some mistakes. Life lessons rarely come during languid hours on a beach with a favorite cocktail in hand. Oscar Wilde had it right: "Experience is simply the name we give our mistakes."

I have a lot of experience!

So, enjoy. Learn. Don't be offended if I seem like I am ranting. Sometimes, I bark a lot, but like my dog, Sirius Black, I don't bite.

Well, not very hard anyway.

Dan John

Tough or Reasonable?

I ANSWER A LOT OF QUESTIONS. I answer my phone, emails and texts. I give a lot of workshops, and I spend a fair amount of time on the internet.

One of the things that recently occurred to me is this: People are wonderful about reading articles and books, but sometimes they miss the point.

As I readily admit, it's my fault. I love experimenting, testing and adapting good training ideas. My mistake is that I write an article or blog post about Tabata front squats or slosh pipes or the Big 21 program, or whatever. This is the start of the problem.

People then read the article and are left with a big issue. And this is the point I'm trying to make here:

Not every good idea, training device or diet
can or should be done at once.

In the past, I've tried to explain this with ideas like "warrior," "king" and "park or bus bench." Recently, I came to discover I have to simplify it even more by using two words:

Reasonable
Tough

1

Reasonable is a fairly tame word, but it's rare today. Clint Eastwood has a marvelous quote (perhaps to an empty chair?):

"I tried being reasonable, I didn't like it."

He perfectly sums up the issue when you apply it to reasonable dieting and reasonable workouts. Let's be honest, they aren't very sexy. A reasonable approach to fitness lacks all the fun adjectives that define our field, but we can actually handle "reasonable" for a fair amount of time.

Tough is more exciting, though.

I don't use any other terms anymore because they may have been copyrighted. I do, however, have a handy tool for any of you wanting to put out an ebook.

Simply pick one word from Column A, one from Column B and one from Column C.

Column A	Column B	Column C
Secrets	Dynamic	Strength
Rules	Metabolic	Mobility
Fundamentals	Easy	Speed
Tools	Simple	Endurance
Vision	Radical	Flexibility
Power	Effortless	Power
Habits	Tactical	Bodybuilding
	Instant	Training
	Combat	Physique
	Brutal	Body
	Punishing	Habits
	Military	Conditioning
	Powerful	

For variation, preface your column A choice with a number, usually "Three," "Five" or "Seven."

Then fill in this form:

The (insert choice from column A) of (insert choice from column B)
(insert choice from column C) program.

I'm as guilty of doing this as anyone, and I hope people take this in the spirit of fun. Feel free to add your own descriptors, of course.

"Tough" workouts are what we tend to look for on the internet. If I write something about a workout that will make a person puke, I'll get emails about it for years.

Are you interested in a tough diet? Maybe I can find you a link for the Velocity Diet. Remember, and this is crucial, the author, Chris Shugart, sold the idea to me (after I begged him to) as a psychological makeover. I have to agree it was psychological, because after twenty-eight days, I felt like a psychopath.

One of the articles that originally turned me on to *T Nation* was Chris's series *Eat Like a Man*. It combined five days of high-protein and high-fat food with a weekend of carbing up.

I adapted this for my athletes at the time, and I still use it as a diet template for strength athletes. *Eat Like a Man* is a reasonable way to approach eating clean for someone who needs to build the qualities of power for a sport.

It's the mix that people miss.

I want to address that here. If you think of a simple quadrant, I'd like to chart out the next few years of your training the following way:

Reasonable Workouts, Tough Diet	Reasonable Workouts, Reasonable Diet
Tough Workouts, Reasonable Diet	Tough Workouts, Tough Diet

Let me address each quadrant.

Reasonable Workouts, Tough Diet

Most of us turn to diet to deal with our fat-loss needs. Having said that, years ago at one of my workshops a noted professor (you'll see why I withhold details in a moment) told me, "Hell, we know how to get you to lose fat and weight: tie you to a tree and come back in three days."

I guess this works, folks, but I struggle to recommend it. Of course, that's going to be the only message some of my readers will take away from this: "Hey, Bubba…tie me to a tree!"

Tough diets work. We all know that. Adherence is an issue, of course, but tough diets do the job. I have issues when I try to diet hard; I turn into a real jackass. But, tough diets get the job done for me. I've lost a lot of weight really fast before lifting meets.

When you dive into a tough diet, you need to do reasonable workouts. What are reasonable workouts? Well, most of the time, I recommend the basic human movements in your training:

Push
Pull
Hinge
Squat
Loaded Carries

For reasonable workouts, I tend to have people live in the fifteen-to-twenty-five total rep range for each movement. You should easily recognize these workouts. The classic workouts live in this range:

3 Sets of 5

5 Sets of 5

3 Sets of 8

The 5 × 5 workout was popularized by Reg Park half a century ago, and it was the basis of most of Arnold's mass-building phases. Five reps of five sets in the bench press, row, deadlift, squat and farmer walks as a finisher is enough work for anyone.

For load, I have a simple formula:

- If you can't do fifteen total reps, the load is too heavy.
- If you can easily do over twenty-five total reps, the load is too light.
- If you're getting those reps and over time increasing the load, you're getting it right. If you haven't added plates in a while, consider this as the real issue behind your lack of progress.

If you're putting all your energy into your eating plan, pick a workout you know you can do. At best, I think you can only follow a hard diet about twice a year. So, pick a training program you know how to do, understand how you tend to recover and, most importantly, know you won't have to use a lot of mental energy in terms of discipline and free will to complete the workouts.

Reasonable Workouts, Reasonable Diet

We should spend most of our training year (probably a better idea is "training decade" or "training lifetime") combining reasonable workouts with reasonable diets.

Years ago at a clinic in Colorado Springs, we were told that our diets should center around three items:

Lean Protein Sources
Vegetables
Clear Water

It's still pretty good advice. I've gone to several workshops in the past where we discussed the Mediterranean Diet, and those two approaches seem to be in step with each other. Now, if you thrive on Atkins, Paleo, Zone, Ornish or whatever, and find it's your way of eating and not your diet, this would be your reasonable diet.

Most of your life should be in this method of reasonable and reasonable. It's reasonable.

Tough Workouts, Reasonable Diet

These are peaking periods of life. As a kid, I called these periods "the big push." As I geared up for track season or an Olympic lifting meet, I knew it was time to spend extra time in the gym, on the track and on the field. The plan expanded. Not only did the quality of movement need to improve, but also the quantity needed to go up.

I visualize peaking as pulling a rubber band in a classroom. If you keep stretching and stretching the band back, it's going to snap in your face. You have to let it go if you want to hit the pretty girl in the fourth row.

And that's the key to tough workouts. Marty Gallagher plans these for twelve weeks; Tommy Kono planned around an eight-week peak; and Dave Turner, my lifting coach, plans eight weeks of increasing load, followed by two weeks of perfect practice and then competition.

The Soviet Squat program I used to do was six weeks of squatting long and hard, three days a week.

If you're truly doing a tough workout, your way of eating has to be built in and simple. Hopefully, your habits are such that you support your training with "big kid" food choices.

For years, I believed that tough training could outrun any diet choices. From my experience and observations from others I trust, as well as some long discussions with some of the brightest minds in sports nutrition, I learned I was wrong. Again.

Make wise food choices while ramping up your training! Like a tough diet, most people can do tough peak programming perhaps twice a year. I've encouraged my older athletes (somewhere around the mid-twenties, not very old!) to think about a minor peak each year, and progress upon that to a major peak later. Again, it's reasonable, doable and repeatable.

Tough Workouts, Tough Diet

Everyone thinks they can do this, but, really, it's a rare bird who can both diet hard and train hard.

Years ago, I had two bodybuilder friends who would help each other train for contests. One day, Lance gave me a call and asked if I could help them train. The other lifter, George, was just a week from the platform. He was living on lettuce. That's it. That's a Tough Diet.

He would do a set, then lie on the ground. It was my job to stir him, pick him up and push him along to the next set. Then,

7

bang, he hit the ground again. When the timed rest period ended, I picked him up again and away we went.

Personally, I can't follow this type of thing. Maybe once every four years or so I could sum up the energy and resources to make a run at training like this, but it would have to be really worth the effort. Something big would have to be on the line.

Yet, when I read about training on the internet, it seems everybody is training with a vengeance and only eating straw mixed with protein powder. Hats off to you!

Off Workouts, Off Diet

This is something I never understood until recently. Every so often, stop worrying about everything. Go to an all-inclusive resort, don't train, eat what you feel like and really forget about things. I learned a lot about humanity on a weeklong cruise, I can tell you that.

For the record, if you haven't suntanned in a while, don't spend day one drinking beer all day in the sun. I saw a lot of that. Also, women who drink heavily in a hot tub seem to leave the tub with fewer clothes than they started. These are lessons I didn't know I needed to know.

The idea behind all of this is fairly obvious. Structure your year or decade in a way where you can swim through various periods of really hard training and some attempts at strict dieting, but with an eye toward long periods of intelligent, progressive resistance training.

When I read about a great diet or training idea, I file it in my expansive collection of material. I let the idea simmer for a while and then find a place in my year where I can apply this new plan.

It's that simple. It's that reasonable.

Goblet Squats 101

THE GREATEST IMPACT I've had on strength and conditioning starts with a story.

Years ago, I was faced with teaching 400 athletes to squat correctly. I attempted move after move and lift after lift, yet I failed each and every time.

I saw glimmers of hope from teaching one kid the Zercher squat (the weight is held in the crooks of the elbows), and a few picked up the pattern when we lifted kettlebells off the ground (called "potato sack squats" because they look like you're picking up a sack of potatoes). But nothing was really working.

The answer was somewhere between a Zercher and a potato squat. It came to me when I was resting between swings with the weight held in front of me like I was holding the Holy Grail. I squatted down from there, pushed my knees out with my elbows and, behold, the goblet squat!

Yes, the squat is that easy. It's a basic human movement; you might just have to be reminded how to do it. Remember, squats don't hurt your knees, but how you perform them can.

Squats can do more for total mass and body strength than probably all other lifts combined. Doing them wrong can do more damage than probably all the other moves, too.

The goblet squat fixes all.

Form: Squat between Your Legs!

Let's start simply. Find a place where no one is watching and squat down.

At the bottom, the deepest you can go, push your knees out with your elbows. Relax. Go a bit deeper. Your feet should be flat on the floor.

For most people, this small movement—driving your knees out with your elbows—will simplify squatting forever.

Next, try this little drill: Stand arms-length from a doorknob or a partner. Grab the knob or the partner's hands, and get your chest up. Up!

Imagine being on a California beach when a swimsuit model walks by. When a guy does this, he immediately puffs up the chest, which tightens the lower back and locks the whole upper body. The lats naturally spread a bit and the shoulders come back a little. (Luckily, this tip works for women, too.)

Now, lower yourself down.

What people discover at this instant is a basic anatomical fact: The legs are not stuck like stilts under the torso. Rather, the torso is slung between the legs.

As you go down, leaning back with arms straight, you'll discover one of the true keys of lifting: you squat between your legs. You don't fold and unfold like an accordion; you sink between your legs.

Don't just sit and read this. Get up and do it!

Now you're ready to learn the single best lifting movement of all time: the goblet squat.

Get Started

Grab a dumbbell or kettlebell and hold it against your chest. With a kettlebell, hold the horns, but with a dumbbell just hold it vertical by one end, like you're holding a goblet against your chest. Hence the name "goblet squats."

Now, with the weight cradled against your chest, squat down with the goal of having your elbows—which are pointed downward because you're cradling the 'bell—slide past the inside of your knees. It's okay to have the elbows push the knees out as you descend.

Stop Thinking. Start Squatting.

Here's the million-dollar key to learning movements in the gym: Let the body teach the body what to do. Try to keep your brain out of it!

Over-thinking a movement often leads to problems. Allow the elbows to glide down by touching the inner knees, and good things will happen.

The more an athlete thinks, the more ways there are to screw things up. Don't believe me? Join a basketball team and get into a crucial situation. Shoot a one-and-one with three seconds to go, down by two points, and get back to me later if you decide thinking was a good idea.

Goblet squats are all the squatting most people need. If the bar hurts in back squats (I won't comment), your wrists hurt in front squat (swallowing my tongue here) and the aerobics instructor has banned you from using the step boxes for your one-legged variations, try the goblet squat.

Seriously, once you grab a 'bell over 100 pounds and do a few sets of ten in the goblet squat, you might wonder how the toilet got so low the next morning.

Foot Placement and Patterning

Where do you place your feet? Do three consecutive vertical jumps, then look down. This is roughly where you want to place your feet every time you squat. The toes should be out a little. You don't want to go east and west, but you want some toe-out.

This drill, along with the goblet squat, teaches patterning. Unless you already have the pattern, you shouldn't move into heavier work.

From Goblets to Grinds

Like goblet squats, I also have my athletes do grinding moves like double-kettlebell front squats (DKFS). The load remains in front, forcing the whole core to stay rigid. Moreover, with two 'bells you can still have your elbows down to push the knees out.

DKFS are exhausting in an odd way: like wrestling an anaconda, you seem to be slowly choking yourself to death. The pressure is also teaching you to stay tight as you continue to grease up and down.

Also, the DKFS seems to really work the upper back in the style called "compression." It's a forgotten method of muscle and strength building where the constant squeezing of a muscle system *is* the movement.

The goblet squat and the DKFS lend themselves to the two greatest workouts I know: the ButtBurner 4000 and the Eagle.

The ButtBurner 4000

I've described the following two exercises in articles online: the Bulgarian goat bag swing and the farmer walk. Look them up to see all the fun you can have with these two.

Grab a kettlebell or dumbbell in the twenty-five-to-sixty-pound range. Go lighter than you think. Now, do this:

- Perform one goblet squat, then one Bulgarian goat bag swing.
- Perform two goblet squats, then two Bulgarian goat bag swings.
- Now, three and three. Work your way up to ten and ten…if you can.

If you just go to fives, that's fifteen reps of each exercise. Tens gets you fifty-five each, and a lot of lost breath. It should go without saying, but I'll say it anyway: build this one up slowly.

This combo will revitalize the entire lower body and teach you to really own both patterns, the hinge and the squat.

The Eagle

The Eagle is named after the school's mascot where I used to teach in Utah. It combines the farmer walk—the basic patterning or teaching tool for loaded carries—with the grinding double-kettlebell front squat.

It's simple:

- Grab two kettlebells (I'm not sure anything else works, but you can experiment) and do five to eight front squats.
- Drop the 'bells to your sides and walk away, perhaps as far as forty meters.
- Do another set of front squats.
- Walk again.

If you can do eight sets of eight with this exercise, plus serious farmer walks in between, you are in rare air.

Greatness with Patience

The mistake most trainees make is they try to move too quickly to complex movements before getting the form down. But greatness resides in those who have the patience to master the patterns first, then add complexity later.

The simple patterns can also make for the most shockingly exhausting workouts. Try the ButtBurner 4000 and the Eagle sometime and see the value of simple, hard work.

The 10,000-Swing Kettlebell Workout

WITHOUT CHALLENGES, the human body will soften. We thrive when we push our boundaries, reach goals and blast personal records. We perform better, we look better and we feel alive.

Get this straight: you're either progressing or regressing. There is no maintenance phase. Moderation in training can easily turn into stagnation. If we want to improve, we have to seek out new challenges, struggle and win.

The 10,000-Swing Kettlebell Workout is just such a challenge. And it will rapidly transform your body in only four weeks.

Battle-Tested Results

I don't write training programs by reading textbooks and studies. I create them in the field, deep in the trenches with real athletes and people whose lives literally depend on their physical abilities.

To create and refine this program, I met several days every week with eighteen other coaches and athletes to put it to the test. Here's what we experienced:

- Everyone got leaner, dropping a waist size or two in twenty workouts.

15

- Every coach or athlete made visual muscular improvements in their physiques, adding lean body mass.
- Every person increased grip strength and greatly increased work capacity and athletic conditioning. We could all train longer and harder when we went back to our normal training programs.
- After the program, every trainee saw a noted improvement in the core lifts. Personal records (PRs) fell like dominos. Full-body strength and power shot through the roof.
- Abs were more visible. Glute strength was tremendously better. The abs and glutes "discovered" how to work again, leading to athletic improvements in sport and in the weightroom.

Program Overview

To do this, in four or five weeks you're going to perform 10,000 proper kettlebell swings. These will be split among twenty workouts. You'll do 500 swings per workout. Between sets of swings, you'll perform low-volume, basic strength exercises.

You'll train four or five days per week. Train two days on, one day off and repeat. Men should use a 24kg kettlebell (53 pounds—we note kettlebell weights in kilos, as my regular readers already know). Women will generally use a 16kg (35 pounds).

This is a stand-alone program. If you feel you're able to do a second workout in the same day, you're under-'belled—you're either not going heavy enough or not training with maximal effort.

The Swings: Clusters, Sets and Reps

Use an undulating rep scheme to reach 500 total reps per workout:

Set 1:   10 reps
Set 2:   15 reps
Set 3:   25 reps
Set 4:   50 reps

You've now completed 100 reps—one cluster. Repeat the cluster four more times for a total of 500 swings.

The Strength Movements

Between sets, experienced lifters often add a low-volume strength movement. The best exercises are:

Press (barbell overhead press or one-arm press)
Dip
Goblet squat
Chinup

Other acceptable choices are the front squat, pistol squat, handstand pushup, wide-grip loaded pullup and the muscle-up. Use a 1-2-3 rep scheme for most movements.

Here's an example using the press:

10 Swings
Press 1 rep
15 Swings
Press 2 reps
25 Swings

Press 3 reps

50 Swings

Rest 30–60 seconds

- For the 1-2-3 lifts, use your five-rep max weight.
- For the dip, you'll need more reps. Use a 2-3-5 rep scheme.
- If you choose to do the program five days a week, on one of those days you'll only do the swings. Leave out the strength work between rounds.
- If you train four days per week, you'll use the strength movements every workout.

You may want to use a different strength movement every workout, rotating between the press, dip, goblet squat and chinup. I also like using two days of chinups and two days of presses.

Remember, choose only one strength movement per workout.

Rest Periods

After each round of ten, fifteen and twenty-five reps, rest thirty to sixty seconds. The first cluster will be easy and you can jam through it. In the later clusters, you'll need the full sixty seconds or more for grip recovery.

After each set of fifty, the rest will extend to three minutes or more. During this post-fifty rest period, perform a corrective. Stretch anything that needs it, like the hip flexors. Just do a mobility movement of choice.

Progression

Time your workouts. Each week you should be getting faster. Your time in workout number twenty should clobber your time in workout number one. For the strength lifts, the goal is to use a weight that's challenging on the first workout and easy by the last workout.

Here's what the program will look like for most lifters:

Day 1

10 Swings
Press 1 rep
15 Swings
Press 2 reps
25 Swings
Press 3 reps
50 Swings

Rest 30–60 seconds; repeat 4 more times.

By the end of the workout, you'll have completed 500 swings and thirty presses.

Day 2

10 Swings
Dip 2 reps
15 Swings
Dip 3 reps

25 Swings
Dip 5 reps
50 Swings

Rest 30–60 seconds; repeat 4 more times.

By the end of this workout, you'll have completed 500 swings and fifty dips. Remember, for dips you're using a 2-3-5 rep scheme, not the 1-2-3 as you do in other lifts.

Day 3: Off

Day 4

10 Swings
Goblet squat 1 rep
15 Swings
Goblet squat 2 reps
25 Swings
Goblet squat 3 reps
50 Swings

Rest 30–60 seconds; repeat 4 more times.

By the end of that one, you'll have completed 500 swings and thirty goblet squats.

Day 5

10 Swings
Chinup 1 rep
15 Swings

Chinup 2 reps
25 Swings
Chinup 3 reps
50 Swings

Rest 30–60 seconds; repeat 4 more times.

By the end of the workout, you'll have completed 500 swings and thirty chinups.

Day 6: Off

Day 7: Off or begin the cycle again

If you begin the cycle again because you want to use the program five days a week, remember to do only the swings during one workout per week.

Swing Technique

The swing is a hip hinge: basically the position you take in a standing long jump. Look for maximum hip bend and minimal knee bend. It is not a squat.

It's a good idea to get some coaching, but the outline is this:

- Begin in the "Silverback gorilla" position.
- Slide the kettlebell back a bit, and vigorously hike the 'bell at your zipper.
- Hinge deeply and let the forearms slide through the thighs.
- Then, snap up to a vertical plank position.

There is no start or finish to a correct swing. The vertical plank is the instant to grab the 'bell and toss it back to the zipper. The hinge causes a rebound and a pop back to the plank.

Ensure the following: the glutes are clenched, lats are "connected" to the shoulders and the arms are snapped directly in front of the body. Don't let the kettlebell float much higher—grab it and toss it back to your zipper. The kettlebell isn't brought overhead.

The swing should be aggressive, explosive and attacked with a high tempo.

What's next?

First, congratulate yourself for actually finishing a program. That's rare in today's world.

You are now in extraordinarily better shape than you were four or five weeks ago. Your training should be poised to take off. I recommend putting these newfound abilities to work with a basic strength template.

Real-Life Training and Eating

MY FAVORITE QUESTIONS about training come from real people. When I say "real," I don't mean that it's usually comic superheroes or hobbits who email me; I'm talking about those great men and women who hold real jobs, serve the community and love to train.

I feel like I can address their issues. I've been the guy with two full-time professions (high school teacher and college instructor), as well as coaching athletes, competing, raising two daughters and living a great life with Tiffini.

Recently, a guy even suggested I must've been given extra hours in the week to do all the things I do, but honestly, there are secrets to surviving and thriving while trying to do "everything" in addition to training and competing at a high level.

Now, these principles aren't for everyone. For example, I got an anonymous comment on my blog when I talked about some friends who died in Afghanistan. Mr. Anonymous found fault with this and noted, "I thought this was a fitness site." I'm reminded of the 14-year-old who repeatedly attacked a famous coach online until it was discovered that, well, he was a 14-year-old jerk. Not everything I write is for everyone.

One of my secrets for busy people is this: train three days a week, but make sure two of the days are back to back. The third day is focused on a weak movement or a full body lift that will challenge you, but not make you dip too deeply into recovery.

Having two days off between each training cluster seems to help people train heavy and hard. But to train this way, there has to be a focus on the other key elements of a total training program.

Brilliant at the Basics

Let's get through the basics first. We'll start with food. I'm a firm believer that a menu for every meal is going to save more time, energy and emotional breakdowns than anything else I can advise. Honestly, it doesn't matter much how you construct a menu, but the genius behind a menu is that it makes shopping easier!

For the past few years we've used a basic menu that usually rotates between three things: a grill night, followed by a chicken "with something" evening, followed by some kind of stew.

Here are six nights of main dishes:

> **Monday:** Steak and salad with veggies
>
> **Tuesday:** Chicken with rice and veggies
>
> **Wednesday:** Jambalaya—prep this the night before and let it slow cook all day.
>
> **Thursday:** Meat Fest! Grill everything in sight plus any veggies worthy of the grill. I toss on pineapple and peaches for dessert.
>
> **Friday:** Chicken enchiladas
>
> **Saturday:** Pot roast or stew—slow cook this all day, too.
>
> **Sunday:** This is often a communal meal with friends and family.

For breakfasts, switch between egg meals and slow-cooked oatmeal. Lunches depend on the situation—school, jobs and life. (Hey, I can't answer everything.)

If you don't like the menu, that's okay, just focus on the point: if you have the right items and a plan, making excellent meals is easy.

On Wednesday and Saturday, I tend to prep the meal, turn on the crock pot and leave for the day. For the busy person, I'd also recommend training on these slow-cooker days. The upside of the crock pot is that the meal is ready when you walk in the door. Scoop and serve. Any mental energy you have in reserve after a long day of work, chores, life or whatever can then be steered into training.

Ever since Josh Hillis told me that the secret to long-term fat loss is to substitute two weekly training sessions for food shopping and food preparation, I've been looking at journals and listening to people about their struggles to "do it all."

If a secret formula to doing it all exists, I'd argue that it begins with making a shopping list. First you shop, then you prep, then you cook and then you eat. If you get this progression right, good things tend to happen.

This is the shopping list we attach to the fridge (I took off items like toilet paper, toothpaste and hygiene products, but yes, I use them too):

- Poultry
- Sausage
- Bacon
- Fish
- Shellfish
- Canned tuna
- Salmon (in the can or fresh)

25

- Eggs (buy them in the five-dozen containers)
- Heavy cream (for coffee)
- Real butter
- Cheese
- Salad greens (everything you can eat raw!)
- Vegetables (I use frozen bags often, but fresh whenever I can)
- Lemons and limes (to sweeten drinks and squeeze onto fish and salads)
- Herbs and spices
- Olive oil
- The best in-season fruit

We keep some rice on hand for filler and side dishes, but we don't do much in the way of pasta and breads. I'm not judging here, but I think as one ages, it seems to help to cut out the cheap grains.

For the busy person, shopping and preparing food is our training. Oh, I know, we all have the discipline of monks when it comes to what we're "going to eat." The problem with most of us is what we actually ate.

I've been suggesting for years that people approach food with a vision beyond the pure present and think about the past, present and future when addressing nutrition.

So, start shopping twice a week—one big full shop like you're preparing to go around the world, and a second shop where you just replenish perishables and pick up the things you forgot during the first shop.

The busier you are, the more important shopping and preparing food becomes. Why? Because over time, to repeat, it's what you eat that made you leaner or fatter, not this glorious diet of things you're going to eat.

Trust me, poor food planning directly leads to poor food choices. You can't out-run, out-bike or out-Zumba several years of tossing piles of sugary food sacrifices on the fires of your hunger.

The Heavy Stuff

After you plan your menu, shop early and spend a little time on prepping, you still need to make time to train. For years I've argued the following for busy people:

1. Train three days a week. One of the days is going to be tight on schedule, so I suggest only doing one lift that day. Choose wisely! More on that below.

2. Corrective exercises, foam rolling, other prehab and rehab work, as well as restorative things like hot tubbing can be done the other days of the week.

3. On the days you train, have your food ready to eat soon after you finish.

4. Training two days in a row and recovering for two full days seems to work for most working people.

Here, the details.

One day a week, try doing just one lift.

My career as an Olympic lifter was resurrected when I finally realized what would be among my greatest insights: If I'm only doing one thing today, I might as well put everything into it.

Clean and Press

I once wrote, "If all you did was clean and press, you could be awesome." Someone actually tried this and emailed to tell me that it didn't work. I didn't know how to explain that I was writing in a style known as hyperbole, but the clean and press really is a one-stop shop to awesomeness.

Look at photos of lifters from the 1960s who extensively employed that lift, and note their massive shoulders and upper body development. Now realize that this will still work. I recommend a barbell, but I made very solid gains with the kettlebell too.

Front Squat

I'm still convinced that the front squat is the best whole body lift for most people. If I'm only doing one lift and it's front squats, I feel like I'm ahead of the curve.

Power Snatch and Overhead Squat Combo

Tony Nielson, a young man I coached for a few years, was the smallest football player on the field, yet I watched him run for more than 200 yards in several games.

He told me it was this power snatch and overhead squat combo move that made the difference and he called it The Exercise. It's a full body movement, and the tension you need to hold the lift trains you in the skills of the super strong.

Dragging a Sled, Pushing a Car or Hill Sprints

If you're short on time, do these at a high intensity. It's the toughest thing I know with the most bang for the buck.

Farmer Walks

I've often challenged people to explore the limits of their physical capabilities with farmer walks. I once did 165 pounds per hand for a competition and felt lousy for days. It's hard to describe the combination of pain, discomfort and intensity that long, heavy farmer walks can breed.

Equipment needs for all these options are minimal and can be done in or from the garage. This is how I've trained for over three decades.

Addressing the other two days a week involves thinking long term about the goals and the approach to training. The following is a program used by a strongman I trained who had two young children. It's best suited for someone who has some time on the weekends and not much the rest of the week.

Strongman

Saturday: Lift Day

> Power snatch
> Power clean
> Front squat
> One-arm lifts (clean and press to max each hand)

My notes to him: Whatever reps and sets you like—I like 3 × 3 or 2 × 5 or singles (after warmups). These are the "meat" sets.

Sunday: Strongman Day

> Power clean and press (singles up to a max)
> Sled dragging, car pushing, hill sprints
> Anything else you need to do with the equipment you have
> Farmer walks (death march style: one set to exhaustion)

Wednesday (or one other day a week)

> One lift: Power clean and press, or power snatch and overhead squat, or front squat. He actually

wanted to handle more, so we did two lifts on the one-lift-a-day workout.

Some kind of carry: Farmer walks or variation

That's it.

Olympic Lifter

I also adapted this for an Olympic lifter. O lifters would normally do the classic lifts on perhaps Saturday and the power moves and squats on Sunday, with the "other" workout being an 80 percent (or less) total day.

Here's an example:

Wednesday

Light total: Snatch and the clean and jerk

Saturday

Snatch
Clean and jerk
Front squats
Farmer walks

Sunday

Power snatch
Power clean
Push jerk
Back squat

Thrower

Highland Gamers often ask about programs to blend a busy professional life with their training. I usually recommend adding as much throwing as they can do, but one nice thing is that the Heavy Weight for Distance seems to help the Light Weight for Distance. The Heavy Hammer and the Light Hammer complement each other, and the Braemar supports the Stone Put.

The caber, in my experience, is best served by doing the Olympic lifts and sled pulls, as well as getting some experience in a lot of Games. I've had a couple people tell me that competing in a Highland Games on Saturday, lifting on Sunday (brave lads indeed!), followed by a single lift and some work on a few events on Wednesdays is one way to balance life and an addiction to Games.

Powerlifter

With some advice, I was able to construct a powerlifting variation that actually works well for many lifters with too much life on their hands.

Wednesday

Bench press (This is why people love this program.)

Saturday

Back squat (But every few weeks deadlift. Most people don't need as much training on the deadlift.)

Bench press

Sunday

Deadlift, squat and bench press assistance exercises

Obviously, you can set this up having the two double days back to back on Monday or Tuesday, with the single lift day on

Before We Go

Friday. With this system you enjoy a free weekend, but it still follows the same principles.

Putting It All Together

Here's an example of a typical week with all the plumbing:

Monday

> Shop and do some basic cooking prep for the week
>
> Restoratives, if necessary

Tuesday

> Restoratives, if necessary
>
> Prepare dinner for the next day

Wednesday

> One lift (front squats or whatever)

Thursday

> Second shop of the week, if necessary
>
> Restoratives, if necessary

Friday

> Prepare the dinner for the next day (or you can BBQ after you train on Saturday, but still prep the food)

Saturday

> Power snatch
>
> Front squat

One-arm clean and press
Farmer walks

Sunday

Press variation
Power clean
Overhead squat
Sled dragging, car pushing or hill sprints

Wrap-up

I admit, there's a lot of information missing, such as how many reps or sets and choosing the appropriate load. What I did cover, however, is the important stuff that busy folks need to get a handle on before they can really improve their physiques or athletic skills.

To that end, my goal wasn't to present the Greatest Workout of All Time or The Ultimate Eight Meals a Day Super Diet, but to combine a real-life scenario and reasonable training principles.

Reasonable is a lost art in the world of fitness.

The Best Ways to Audit Your Program

As I SLIDE INTO A NEW ERA in my career, schools and teams are increasingly asking me to evaluate the direction of their strength-training programs. This section will describe my basic tool kit for that.

Few people take the time to march through the simple steps to assess and evaluate their training as a whole. Certainly, we've made great strides in assessing movement with the Functional Movement Screen (FMS), and we're miles ahead in the area of blood tests, MRIs and sonograms for evaluating what's going inside without having to use a knife and scissors.

However, most programs still lack a simple audit, monthly or yearly, to look under the hood to see if they're really filling the gaps.

And that's exactly what I do first—I look for the gaps in a program.

The Fundamentals

Do you do the fundamental human movements?

Push

Pull

Hinge

Squat

Loaded Carries
Everything else—usually groundwork or tumbling

It stuns me when I see a program that claims to be balanced, yet ignores what I see as key movements. I've covered these movements before, and people were frankly surprised to find that something as simple as the basic loaded carry could so quickly make such a difference in a training program.

Step one is to fill the gaps. I still enjoy a few sessions a month of yoga, and recently, as the sweat streamed across my eyelids, I decided to evaluate it. Clearly it's not a lifting program, but save for loaded carries, it involves all of my fundamental human movements. Following the directions we're given, we'll swim through pushing, pulling, squats (the "awkward" poses), hinges and groundwork.

And that's a full forty-five-minute session of groundwork. I noted in a recent yoga session that I was rolling around the ground from position to position for almost half the session. And getting up and down off the ground is becoming a rarity for the adult population.

A Brazilian research group came up with a very interesting little test of rising from and lowering to the floor. If only your feet and butt are needed, you get a five rating. If one limb hits—knee, elbow or hand—you get a four. Two hits and you receive a three. Their study found connections between longevity and the score on this test.

Literally, we need to roll around on the ground more. I have one bit of advice for my older clients: watch all the television you want, but you must be on the floor when you do. Try it! You'll find soon that you roll, pivot, twist, change and flop the whole show. It's a cheap workout.

When I assess most programs, groundwork is usually a few sets of crunches and that's it. Groundwork, tumbling and wrestling can transform a program in a few weeks, but few will adopt this strategy.

Something as simple as the rolling portion of the Turkish getup is a good start. I suggest everyone begin adding more work from the floor.

The Strength Audit

Auditing a program is difficult. I like two sets of numbers, but with both of them, there's an additional and important step.

First, count the total number of reps in a program over perhaps something as short as a two-week block. Let's use this example:

Pushes: 250
Pulls: 75
Hinges: 15
Squats: 135
Loaded Carries: 10

Here I'm trying to show that the push-to-pull ratio is unsound. One to one would obviously be better, and I might even go to a two-to-one ratio in the offseason.

The problem is the hinges and farmer walks and, honestly, they're always the problem in this audit. If those fifteen hinges were all serious and heavy deadlifts, I'd suggest that business was being taken care of. Doing 500 kettlebell swings with a fifty-pound kettlebell might be the ticket to general conditioning and fat loss, but it might not be as impactful as a single 500-pound deadlift.

Farmer walks and the whole family of loaded carries are another issue. "Down and back" might count for two reps, but those two reps might take everything you have to complete.

But as I tell the gym owners, counting the reps at least gives you an insight into what you're doing. Even when most people know they're doing too many pushes, it's hard to cut back as they appear in the warmup through the pushups and a host of transition movements. Dozens of pressing-based machines at their disposal also provide a powerful temptation.

There's another tool that also works wonders. It's so simple you may miss its value: Every time you include an exercise, mark a check next to the exercise on your master list.

If I think front squats are important and I have 150 training sessions a year, and the front squat ends up with 120 checks, I can assume my mouth and my program are on the same general course.

It also gives insights into a program's variation issues. For example, let's say these are your press variations:

Overhead press with barbells
Single-arm overhead press with dumbbells
Single-arm overhead press with kettlebells
Double-overhead press with dumbbells
Double-overhead press with kettlebells
Seesaw presses with kettlebells
Incline press with all the above options
Decline press with all the above options
Push, press and push jerk variations of all the above

And these are your squat variations:

Back squat

Well, look, there's a bit of an imbalance. Either you believe the back squat is the answer to any and all questions, or you need to rethink your squat variations.

As far as loaded-carry variations, it's tough to really find some that don't look like idiocy after a while, but some variations from suitcase carries to pushing trucks will keep things fresh.

The Standards

Once you see the gaps, the program's standards suddenly become clear. I've felt for years that my "Standard Standard" isn't a bad start.

In this idea, the clean, front squat and bench press should be "around" the same number. I train athletes, and this formula has withstood the test of time. If you bench 500 and get crippled with a 135-pound front squat, we need to talk about balance.

Wil Heffernan offers the following wonderful standards:

Bench press: Bodyweight × 15

Back squat: Bodyweight × 15

Pullups: Bodyweight × 15

45 honest pushups in a minute (in an honest pushup the elbows lock out; the chest touches a partner's clenched fist on the ground)

24 strict horizontal body rows in a minute (the chest must touch the bar; the legs are elevated)

"Best Lifts All Time" tend to favor genetic superstars, but standards reward hard work. A program's standards should reflect the goals of the program and the kind of training we're doing.

I suppose this is why I'm such a fan of Jim Wendler's 5/3/1 program, consisting of bench press, deadlift, squat and overhead press. Jim arranges these lifts into a simple weekly format and, for more information, buy his book! By adding some sled pulling and farmer walks, a tumbling session, and some daily groundwork and technical practice, we could make this a gapless program.

Using this template, I can establish a number of standards that are obvious and attainable. I've said for years that a high school boy needs to deadlift 315 pounds, and that 400 pounds is an appropriate goal for most football players. Wendler's program gets the athlete to these basic standards.

Most facilities should use some kind of "magic device" that will show the athlete "if you do this, you should be able to squat that." I can't beat this little program.

Fast Twitch Fountain of Youth

The final area I look for in evaluating training programs is fast twitch muscles. Years ago, I picked up a book by Phil Campbell called *Ready, Set, Go! Synergy Fitness*. The book underscored the joke we had in track and field.

"Go to a Masters track meet. Look at the distance runners as they go by and guess their age. To get it right, minus ten (because distance runners look much older than they are on their birth certificate). Then go watch the throwers, jumpers and sprinters. Guess their age, but to get it right, add ten years at least."

Fast twitch keeps us young. It's also crucial in a strength program. How you get it can vary from doing the quick lifts to jumping to sprinting to pushing a Prowler, but you need to reach into those fibers that make you, as the commercial used to say, "run faster and jump higher!"

For a middle-aged person, yoga will do marvels for mobility, flexibility, basic movements, groundwork and recovery. Toss in some presses, goblet squats and a few weekly sprints and you have everything covered.

Sprinting digs a deep hole in recovery, though. For high school track and field sprint corps, I have a "rule of 1,200." Never go hard for more than 1,200 meters in a session. Now that can be two 600s, twelve 100s or whatever, but it's very hard to sprint fast for more than that in a training session.

Stress-Free Auditing

Auditing a training program can be simple. Ask yourself, "What are the gaps in my movements?" Try the two-week test of counting reps, and then think about the quality of the movements.

If you really want to look deeply into your training, chart the movements over a year-long period. Extremes either way might need discussion. For example, my sophomore year in college, I only did five lifts the whole year! Some of you might have dozens of variations and wonder why you're not getting stronger.

Next, address these two final keys: are you balanced in your standards and do you explore training with explosive fast-twitch moves? Ignoring either of these is the royal road to frustration.

Audit your training and address the issues you find.

The Secret of Loaded Carries

THE GAME CHANGER: Tapping into the right movement can radically change your body.

Find the missing ingredient and you'll build more muscle faster, drop fat quicker and kick any ass on any field of play. And I'm going to tell you what that missing ingredient is for most weight-trained people. Ready?

It's the loaded carry.

The loaded carry does more to expand athletic qualities than any other thing I've attempted in my career as a coach and an athlete. And I do not say that lightly.

Ted's Story

A few years ago, I worked with an athlete named Ted. Now, Ted's issue was interesting: He was a solid powerlifter and very good at the two Olympic lifts, the snatch and the clean and jerk. In other words, he wasn't a wannabe, a beginner, a neophyte or an internet warrior. Ted was the real deal.

When he came to visit for a week, there wasn't a ton of stuff I could help him with in the weightroom. A pointer here and there and I was finished.

So, being finished, we went outside for a "finisher," and I asked, "Would you rather do carries, walks or sleds?"

"I've never done any of those things," Ted said.

Good, I thought. I can help.

Within seconds of his first attempt with the farmer bars weighing 105 pounds apiece, he was like a stumbling drunk. He could pull hundreds of pounds off the floor but didn't have the stability—the cross-strength—to handle more than a few feet with the bars.

Next I tried to get him to walk holding a 150-pound bag to his chest. He gasped for breath and nearly choked to death. Literally, his human "inner tube" had almost no range past five seconds.

I'd found Ted's missing movement. Ted needed to carry heavy stuff.

A few weeks later, I get the call: "Dan, you're a genius! My deadlift has gone up and I'm just thicker all over!" He'd increased his lift from the low 500s to the high 500s.

Humbled coach blushes but nods knowingly.

I was not surprised. Again, in my coaching toolbox, nothing has been a game changer like loaded carries.

Are you ready to learn how to do a few variations? Good. Let's do it.

Loaded Carry Variations

I break loaded carries into three main categories.

Category One: Weights in the Hand

These are the simplest and most recognized: grab a dumbbell or kettlebell and walk away.

One-Handed Carries

Waiter walk: The weight is held with a straight arm overhead, like a European waiter in a café. This is usually the lightest of the carries and does wonders for shoulders.

Suitcase walk: Grab the weight in one hand like a suitcase and walk. The obliques on the other side of the weight will want to have a discussion with you the next day.

Rack walk: Usually done with kettlebells, hold the 'bell in the racked position, where the weight is on the chest in the "clean" position. This is a fairly remedial move, but it can teach you about how the abs work.

Two-Handed Carries

The press walk: This is just a double-'bell waiter walk, but the weights come alive as you move. Warning: Do not do this to failure. It looks dangerous because, well, it is dangerous.

Farmer walk, the king of carries: Go as heavy as you can with 'bells in both hands, just like in a Strongman competition. This can be done really heavy for short distances or lighter for great distances. My favorite variation is really heavy for great distances.

Double-rack walk: Same as above, but with two kettlebells. Again, it's a learning move and a great way to teach us to breathe under stress.

Cross walk: This is a waiter walk in one hand, while doing the farmer walk in the other. It's a very interesting way to learn to lock down the midsection during movement.

Category Two: Bags, Packs and Vests

This group includes backpacks, sandbags and weighted vests. Personally, I still prefer an old duffle bag or a field pack.

Go to a store where you can buy either water softener salt or salt for de-icing. For about ten dollars, you can get 150 pounds of salt. Sand is easier to find in some places. Get whatever is cheap.

The basic bag carries are simple. It comes down to either backpacking the bag, holding the weight over the shoulders like a squat bar or bear hugging it.

A backpack or vest setup is ideal as it leaves your hands free.

Bear hugging is a great training tool, as the weight is not unlike Zercher squats: the internal pressure is building, the breath is choked off by the weight on the chest, and squeezing it hard in order to hold it is adding to all the problems. All in all, it's just nothing but fun.

Category Three: Sleds

In the category of "carries" I also include sleds, pushing cars, going up hills (forward and backward) and all the various pushing devices available in good gyms these days.

It's simple: Hook up a sled either with a harness or weight belt and tow away!

The Real Secret

Each of these moves works well alone. But here's the "secret" to taking loaded carries over the top: combine them.

Hook yourself up to a dragging sled. Then don a 150-pound backpack. Now pick up farmer walk implements weighing 150 each. That combination is one of the most difficult things I've done in my life. You try it.

Obviously, some combinations don't work as well as others. Cross walks and overhead walks of any kind are usually epic failures when combined with something else. Fun to watch, though.

How Much and How Often?

I've had high school sophomores use eighty-five pounds per hand in the farmer bars, and we had more advanced athletes work up to 155 pounds per hand. I've done more in competition and wouldn't suggest you do it…yet.

A bag of salt or sand weighing fifty pounds is an eye-opener. I also recommend going to a home supply place to get a wheelbarrow shell (just the green part that holds stuff), string a rope through it and connect it to a weight belt. For weights, start out with cement pieces or a bunch of rocks.

So, with two dumbbells or kettlebells, a wheelbarrow shell, a weight belt, a backpack, some sand and some rocks, you can train at the top of the food chain.

How far? How many? How long?

Well, I know you hate this, but…it depends. I usually tell people to first try every movement from waiter walks to cross walks. Hug a bag to your chest and walk around. Don't go far and don't do much. Just get a sense of things. Rarely do we do more than "down and back" with each move, as we strive to keep adding elements each set.

So:

- Suitcase walk
- Farmer walk
- Suitcase walk with backpack
- Farmer walk with backpack
- Sled pull
- Sled pull with bear-hugged bag
- Sled pull with backpack
- Sled pull with backpack and farmer bars

That's eight movements down and back with minimal equipment and a lot of work.

The "how far" question is usually answered with "not very." You'll find out why.

Do some kind of loaded carry three times a week, but only one of the days should be "everything." You want to be aggressive and intense when you attack these movements.

Farmer walks and bear hug carries are my personal favorite moves, and they tend to be some of the best bang-for-the-buck choices.

Three Weeks Is All It Takes

Get back to me after doing these for three weeks. Obviously, your grip will be better. Your legs will be stronger. You'll discover that the weightroom isn't that tough any more. You'll look leaner but will be bigger.

Now get to work.

The Big Five of Getting Big

I KNOW A VERY NICE GUY. Really, he's the kind of guy you would let watch your house and take care of your dog. He asked me a good question.

"Dan, what's the secret to getting big?"

Ah. That question. I really think (put on your sarcasm ears, kids, so you don't miss it) this is the very first time the question has ever been asked!

The questioner has a great life and a lot going on for him. He's in a desperate pursuit for mass gains, but he misses the mark terribly. Oh, he has the powders, the protein bars and the programs littered all over his apartment and small gym space.

What's he missing? Well, I'm going to tell you the "secrets" in just a moment, but I had to remind him of a couple of things first.

I explained to him how we're all lucky to have made it this far. I'm convinced each of us ignores the role of just good old-fashioned luck in our survival. If some of the new DNA research is true, there were, at one time, only 600 people who would eventually develop into humanity.

The numbers were, and continue to be, against our survival. I can think of many small moments in my life where someone pulled me out of a pool or the ocean, or convinced me to do something different than the idiotic thing I was about to do.

And I hated to tell him this, but survival seems to favor the skinny. It's easier to pull a guy out of the pool when he doesn't weigh much.

We're lucky. Most people don't acknowledge the amazing number of fragile moments that came together to make you "you."

How you approach the rest of your life—your attitude about your future—is one of the keys to lifelong fitness. So, while I applaud the goal of getting big, take a moment to enjoy your health, your wealth and the sun rising in the morning.

Having said that, let's help my friend get big.

My buddy could be the 97-pound weakling pictured in the ads for the Charles Atlas course that defined strength for a few generations, but he wants to live life BIG!

Well, of course I gave him my Big Five of Getting Big. They're old, dusty, rusty and moldy ideas, but even if they already know them, I can still bet most guys don't follow them.

1. First, stop with all the plates.

There we were trying to get a workout and he slaps those two-and-a-half-pound plates at the ends of the bar for his next set.

"What are you doing?" I asked.

"I'm going up."

Not very damn quickly, I can tell you that.

If I can make one suggestion that'll do wonders for most, it's to stop using twos or fives or tens. Just use the bigger plates.

For a while, just use 45s and 25s. Yes, it's going to be harder and heavier and you're going to be nervous sometimes making the big jumps, but once you begin doing this you'll notice you're becoming bigger and stronger.

Now this may shock you, but it's true: *Strong guys are often big guys.*

You may or may not like this advice, but at least try a few workouts without using your calculator and spreadsheets and just move some iron.

2. Eat some damn food!

There are two issues here.

First, I always remember a quote I heard during a weightlifting workshop: "Never have there been so many gathered together to discuss lifting and so few who looked like they ever had lifted weights!"

But they must have been legitimate weightlifters. After all, I kept hearing the snap and crackle of protein bar wrappers being torn apart every two hours.

These guys ate every two hours on rigid schedules, but never actually looked like they ate anything! Was it too little nutrition or did they need to eat at one hour and fifty-eight minutes? I have no idea, but it was fun to watch them eat twenty dollars a day in bars and then, later that night, not spend any money at the real bars.

This generation saddens me, I must say.

My second point on food is simple. The following is from my book *Mass Made Simple*:

> *Honestly, seriously, you don't know what to do about food? Here is an idea: eat like an adult. Stop eating fast food, stop eating kid's cereal, knock it off with all the sweets and comfort foods whenever your favorite show is not on when you want it on, ease up on the snacking and—don't act like you don't know this—eat more vegetables and fruits.*

Really, how difficult is this? Stop with the whining. Stop with the excuses. Act like an adult and stop eating like you live in a television commercial. Grow up.

Here you go: eat food and drink water and, if you take supplements, buy quality stuff. Food should be something you can imagine where it originally came from. There are no Twinkie Trees. Sorry.

Oh, and that "Twinkie Diet" that hit the news about the professor losing 27 pounds? Let me comment: he was eating 1,800 calories a day. 1,800 calories is a snack to someone who wants to attain bigness.

3. Start living big.

You need to sleep big. Seriously, you need to learn to go to bed early, wake up late, lounge around, and take naps.

I remember learning that the Cuban National Weightlifting Team slept nine hours a night and took three-hour naps. Whether it's true or not isn't the issue; it supports a point. Later, of course, I found out what taking a "siesta" really meant (knock, knock, wink, wink, nudge, nudge), and maybe that's not a bad idea either.

I'm convinced that for whatever reason the hours of sleep before midnight are "better" than the hours after midnight. Now that I live in a quiet area that gets dark early, I've noticed it's easy to go to sleep earlier.

Oh, I should note I don't watch reality television, nor do I have an ongoing internet chat relationship with a really hot girl who lives several states away. After dinner, I have a "tipper," read a book or talk and ease off into the night. Sadly, I now wake up early in the day ready to work and take on the world. I sure do miss waking up crabby and barking at everyone and needing six pots of coffee.

Big, strong guys have a unique ability to sit. They lounge at a high level. They can turn lunch into a marathon. Ease off, Twitchy, and let yourself grow.

4. Look for technical mastery.

Most people ignore the fourth principle of getting big. Technical mastery is a key to true life in Bigocity. Oh, before I get going, PLEASE don't tell me you follow this principle because you follow the instructions on the leg extension machine for technical mastery.

If you don't know what I'm talking about, go to any spa or facility with machines. In the complex where I used to live, we had about five machines with detailed directions on how to adjust the machine to height, leg length (I'm not kidding), how to grip the handles (when working your legs), how to breathe and warnings about exertion.

Each machine has a list of about ten things to do before attempting to move.

Compare this to a 500-pound squat. In my prime, I don't remember seeing a checklist near the rack, the platform or the bench. If you don't take the time to learn to squat correctly, to bench correctly, and to move the big iron correctly, you won't survive to move the big iron correctly. There are dozens of sites, DVDs, books and other resources available for you to learn these lessons. It's then up to you to master the technique.

Listen, this isn't an "agree to disagree" issue. It's more like you telling me that you count to ten like this: 1-2-5-3-6-4-7-9-8-10. No, that's wrong.

If you don't have technical mastery, you won't survive moving big weights. Learn it early and then pile on the plates.

5. Rely on rest periods.

My fifth and final point is something I've been trying to explain for years. It's rest periods. Skinny, weak guys are obsessed with short rest periods.

Oh, they definitely have value in some workouts. Ten seconds is hell in the Tabata front squat workout. The classic 30/30 workout where you alternate thirty seconds of movement with thirty seconds of rest can be a killer. When I do my Transformation Program and map out one-minute rests between sets of eight, I'm dying by the third set.

Those are all conditioning workouts, whatever that means in this day and age. If you want to get big, well, toss out all of that. Seriously. Out.

Years ago I was preparing for a local lifting meet with Dave Turner, and we'd settled on a last attempt in the clean and jerk with 385. Dave's idea was to start with 363, jump to 374, and then take a new personal record on the last attempt.

"Um, Dave," I said, nice as can be, "I'll be the only guy left in the meet then, right?"

"Sure."

Then, let's go to Plan B.

You see, at the time lifters were given three minutes if they had to "follow themselves," meaning there were no other competitors left on deck. That meant I could possibly have to make three maximal lifts in around eight minutes. It just wasn't going to happen. We decided on 308 (to ensure a total), 341 (the original "last warmup"), and 385. I made them. It was still eight minutes, but I could easily recover from the first two loads.

That's what my skinny friend doesn't understand. He thinks 100% for him is the same as 100% for someone really big and strong.

As a young lifter, I could never understand why the Olympians would take weeks off after the event. As I grew older and stronger, it made more sense. It takes time to recover from the big iron. It might be measured by the calendar, but not by the stopwatch. If you don't understand that yet, you will when you start lifting big.

I have some yardsticks regarding what I call a male advanced beginner in the lifting world:

Bodyweight bench press

Double-bodyweight deadlift

You should also be able to clean and front squat your bodyweight too.

Folks, that's a pretty low level of strength. Although you "could" play high school football at this level, I'd still suggest you keep coming back to the weightroom.

You can time all the rest periods you want with your timer, your calculator and that app you got off the web, but until you get to at least the advanced beginner stage, you have to worry more about weight on the bar than short rest periods.

Skinny guys do forced reps with 135. They also do that workout where they strip tens off the sides of the bar and keep repping out.

Listen, add more plates. Rest more. Grow. Get stronger.

For the record, I got a note from my skinny young friend that he'd put on a lot of bodyweight in a few weeks by "eating everything in sight" and lifting heavier.

And, yes, it can be that simple.

Four Ways to Fire Up Work Capacity

WORK CAPACITY IS THAT ABILITY to perform work, which determines your level of fitness that will, in turn, determine your level of preparedness. It's an issue for people in the military and in collision sports. In fact, lifters, off-season athletes and pretty much anybody and everybody would benefit from improving work capacity.

Here are four ways to do it, three you've probably heard of and one that may surprise you.

Groundwork

Literally at your feet is one of the best pieces of training equipment I know of for building work capacity—the ground. As a child, I did judo and it built a lifelong appreciation for falling, breaking the fall and the art of subtle movement. It also taught me to roll in every direction, cartwheel, leap over people (more fun than you think) and not break anything in the process.

When Ken Shamrock's book *Inside the Lion's Den* came out, I saw a gap in my coaching. He recommended a great deal of basic tumbling, and I was inspired to program the same things I'd learned as a child.

- Forward roll
- Shoulder roll
- Various crawls
- Cartwheels
- Basic tumbling combinations

The impact on our athletes was immediate. A shoulder injury plague disappeared, soccer players learned to pop back up into play like football players, and the general conditioning of everyone improved overnight.

Basic rolling—and I include the Turkish getup here—can also be considered dynamic foam rolling. Rolling around opens things up and seems to knit us back into place at the same time.

Aside from teaching a valuable skill, tumbling and rolling can improve work capacity and simultaneously change body composition. You'll be surprised how tired and sweaty you get from doing five reps of tumbling moves.

Hills, Drags, Loaded Sprints

The next great way to build capacity is running, pushing or dragging with a load. Generally, I put these activities in the same category as loaded carries. Hill sprints have been my basic coaching tool for training explosiveness to throwers since…forever.

For whatever reason, it's nearly impossible to hurt yourself while sprinting uphill. It's certainly self-limiting when a tired athlete doesn't have the energy to hurt himself.

Running downhill, of course, is another issue. I don't trust 250-pound throwers sprinting downhill. There's this thing called "physics," and even though I don't understand the math, I can only see bad things happening from small refrigerators hurling themselves down a hill.

Today, you can mimic hill sprints in the gym using Prowlers or sleds. The trouble is, people overload these implements, which takes the "snap" out of the movement. It's a matter of feel, of course, but both too light and too heavy make these exercises less valuable.

There are so many factors involved (asphalt versus grass, the make and model of the device, the number of runners on the bottom) that I can't give load recommendations, but err on the side of lighter. If the action makes you look more like a sprinter and less like a plough horse, you have it right.

Don't "wallow," as Coach Maughan used to tell us at Utah State when we did sled pulls.

Complexes Made Simple

For years, I've introduced complexes to my athletes at times when I thought we needed a bit more muscle mass. My definition of a complex is simple. A complex is a series of lifts back to back where you finish the reps of one lift before moving on to the next. The barbell only leaves your hands or touches the floor after all of the lifts are completed. You can do them with barbells, dumbbells or kettlebells.

The key to organizing a complex is to make sure the bar passes over your head in some kind of logical manner. In other words, if you do rows followed by back squats, how did the bar get there? You need at least one intermediate move to get the bar onto your shoulders for the back squats. I try to have the bar pass backward over the head after a few lifts, but I only pass it forward again once.

When you initially try these, use a broomstick. It'll save some wasted effort and awkwardness if you get the hang of the transitions before you add weight.

When I want to increase work capacity and build mass, I only assign one complex for a six-week assault on bulking.

There are several reasons for this. First, it helps to master the combination of movements. I can whip up a new complex in a manner of minutes, and that may be great if you're in love with variations, but sadly, those with the most variations in their training are usually the weakest and skinniest.

Second, this complex has a nice mix of pushing, pulling, squatting and bending with just enough rest between to allow some recovery.

Finally, complexes are, well, complex. I don't want you putting the bar down and trying to remember how to do this or that. I want you to stress and strain for those last seconds.

Try to recall my definition—a complex is a series of lifts performed back to back where you finish the reps of one lift before moving on to the next. The barbell only leaves your hands or touches the floor after all of the lifts are complete.

With that in mind, here's my favorite complex:

- Row
- Clean
- Front squat
- Military press
- Back squat
- Good morning

If the workout calls for eight repetitions, you need to do eight rows, followed by eight cleans, eight front squats, eight military presses, eight back squats and then eight good mornings.

Don't load up the bar the first few times you attempt these, though. Trust me, it's a bad idea.

Tumbling, loaded sprints and complexes are amazingly simple ways to increase work capacity.

The other method is simple, too, but it may not make sense at first.

The Deprivation Effect

I've heard hundreds of testimonials from people who bravely assert that they're going to start some tough diet next Monday. These seemingly brave people have all the energy and drive to win several Super Bowls, Olympic championships and World Wars.

Of course, come next Tuesday, I often get a long list of excuses as to why "this ONE time" they couldn't adhere to the diet program.

I know why. Deprivation is tough. Humans seem to be hard-wired to not being able to do something. Yet amazingly, deprivation often works wonders.

If your favorite gym closes down, you might suddenly notice the park next to your house is actually a perfect training facility. Arnold used this method in his youth. He'd gather up his friends, go off into the woods with their equipment and train. He'd choose a lift and just keep doing it over and over. There's more to this, but the idea of leaving the comfy confines of the normal gym to venture out will change your methods of training forever.

Many of us didn't allow our sons and daughters to watch TV on school nights. Maybe they miss some popular culture, but they become voracious readers and get skilled at games and sports. That's the way deprivation works. You give up something and gain something that might even be better.

Probably the only thing you shouldn't deprive yourself of, though, is sleep. That tends to be a dead end for most people.

So, add the floor (tumbling), some hills (sleds and the like) and a classic way of barbell training (complexes) to your training to increase your work capacity.

In addition, consider increasing your work capacity by depriving yourself of some things—the perfect gym, the best equipment, TV or whatever it is that keeps you from focusing on living a full life.

It's hard to manage, but it's completely worth the effort.

Nine Great Ideas to Improve Your Workouts

MY LIFE CHANGED when I read Earl Nightingale's *Lead the Field*. Nightingale, a survivor of the attack on Pearl Harbor, was a pioneer of motivational work. His key point can be summarized like this:

"We become what we think about."

I've often argued that we need to spend more time thinking about our training, and below we'll look at three ideas in each of the three key areas of strength training—repetitions, workouts and programming.

Three Ideas about Reps

1. Use countdown reps

A few years ago, Brian Oldfield, a former world record holder in the shot put, and I were talking about lifting, when he told me about a Polish school where the athletes were lifting. Instead of counting up like most Americans, the kids counted down, like a takeoff at NASA—5, 4, 3, 2, 1. Brian loved the idea because the concept of "Blast Off" was perfect with the explosive nature of training.

I'm a huge fan of 5 × 5 workouts, and this little change can be very valuable in those. The second to last set is mentally the toughest, and this is a way to get around that problem.

2 The And-One Method

Bill Witt, a throwing-coach legend, gave me another idea that deals with the higher reps often used for hypertrophy. But for those of us who have spent our lives thinking that five reps qualifies as "high reps" and anything above six is cardio, it takes a mental shift to get in those higher reps during a workout.

Bill's simple answer is "and-one." "And" is the first rep and "one" is the second. A set of ten looks like this:

> *"And-One-And-Two-And-Three-*
> *And-Four-And-Five."*

You've done ten reps, but you've only counted five. Ten reps can be a struggle by rep eight or nine for a lot of us, but this method somehow tricks the mind. Much of training is a mind game, so accept it and play.

3. Embrace "ish"

Steve Ledbetter has an idea that really works well with competitive athletes who aren't competing in the iron game. He simply says "ish."

The best example of "ish" is John Powell's approach to the 5 × 5. Each year, he'd set a goal of doing a weight for five sets of five. If he chose 365 as his target weight, he'd plop down on the bench once a week and test himself.

365 for 4
365 for 3
365 for 1
365 for 1
365 for 1

He'd then add up the total reps of the workout (ten in this case). As the weeks and months progressed, he'd slowly work up into the teens, and then the low twenties. With a serious enough weight, it could take months to build up to the full twenty-five reps of a 5 × 5 workout.

The upside of this plan may not be obvious—it allows you to use heavy weights and slowly, steadily, build up the volume. Progress in life and the weightroom is as "ishy" as I can imagine.

Three Ideas About Workouts

1. Punch the clock

I've been preaching the idea of "punch the clock" workouts for almost a decade. Those are sessions where you just show up and do the work. If you have a plan, you follow it. If you have a preprinted workout, you finish it.

Like a craftsman, much of our training is just showing up and doing stuff. It's also the kind of training that builds a reliable system over time. But there are times when you need to leave it all on the floor. Sadly, as in my second thought below, "leaving it all on the floor" can actually happen.

2. Perform challenges

I like to call these workouts and short windows of training "challenges." Challenges like my Farmer Walk Challenge and my 315 Deadlift Challenge. What fun they are!

I also call these "Kill Yourself Workouts." They're great, but you can only do these for about three weeks before you die.

In junior high, our first football game was cancelled, so our coaching staff decided to sneak in a few extra days of double sessions. We had three-and-a-half weeks of two-a-day training sessions, during which our team dropped from seventy football players to about twenty-five. Our season was a disaster, as we could never really come back from the load of all the training.

Most gyms that push "balls to the wall" training every session tend to have huge dropout rates, lots of physical therapy issues, and tend to close rather quickly. You certainly can do anything, but there's wisdom in not doing everything all the time.

3. The Hangover Rule

I've had conversations with people from all kinds of sports and I've noticed a pattern—their lifetime best effort was often performed the morning after a series of bad decisions, many of them being made at something like a bachelor party.

Many of the stories included puking in flowerbeds, so perhaps that's the actual secret, but more likely it's this: *Expecting nothing or very little from a training session or competition often allows one to stretch and expand far beyond the usual constraints.*

Do you have to be hung over? No. When I was eighteen my coach left on a road trip, and I had to train without him. When I walked in the door, my clean and jerk PR was 270 pounds. But I was feeling good and I clean and jerked 271 for a new record. It felt easy, so I did 282. Then I made 292.

Dan Curiel walked in and said, "Try 137.5 kilos. You can make it." That's 303 pounds. I made the lift and broke the 300-pound barrier. I'd added thirty-three pounds to my personal record in half an hour.

Why? How? Don't know and didn't ask. I've learned extraordinary training sessions and days just pop out of nowhere, and you have to enjoy your dance with these rare moments of life.

Three Ideas About Programming

1. Look for gaps

In programming, I keep my eye on two basic concepts that open the way for a third. First, and I know you know this, I'm all about looking for gaps in training. Gaps consist of anything you should be doing but aren't. Here's my list of the fundamental human movements (yes, I know you know this by now, too!):

> *Push*
> *Pull*
> *Hinge*
> *Squat*
> *Loaded carry*
> *Everything else*

Most people skip squats and loaded carries. I've argued for years that just adding goblet squats and farmer walks to workouts will take care of most training problems.

When Mike Brown and I train, he does the math after every session to see if there's balance across our movements. It's always a challenge, of course, to judge a 700-pound deadlift (hinge) against light goblet squats to see if there's balance, but just looking for gaps is my sole goal.

2. Meet the standards

Next, logically, come the standards. I've worked on dozens of standards and shared them in the past.

For instance, I've found that when a high school boy does over 200 pounds in the bench press, clean and front squat, good things seem to happen. Here's my Big Blue Club, the basic standard for being a varsity athlete:

> *Power clean: 205 pounds*
> *Deadlift: 315 pounds*
> *Back squat: 255 pounds*
> *Front squat: 205 pounds*
> *Standing press: 115 pounds*
> *One-arm bench: 70 pounds (5 right/5 left)*
> *Power clean and jerk: 165 pounds*
> *Bench press: 205 pounds*

This should be easy enough to do all in one training session. I also have standards for pushups (forty-five in a minute), pullups (five real ones) and horizontal rows (twenty-four in a minute—keep the feet on a bench so it doesn't become a leg exercise).

I'll continue to work on standards for adults to include the untrained and the detrained as well as those on the road to mastery.

3. Trust Your intuition

You must trust yourself and train with intuition. A decade ago, it was called instinctive training, but it's simply this: when you've put the time, effort and energy into your training, you can sometimes "get a hint" that you need to do X, Y or Z.

Many of my morning sessions are done with a group of people from various ages and athletic backgrounds. I often ask, "Does anyone need to work on anything?" Sometimes a participant will say something very simple and direct, and the group will all start working on this issue or problem.

Generally, within a few minutes, we all agree that we needed the same corrections.

Now that doesn't mean every day is going to be arm day because the Force is telling you to work biceps.

If you keep a running log of checking your gaps and trying to fulfill certain standards, you can allow yourself a lot more flexibility in your training because you can see over a week or a month whether your "instinct" is right or wrong.

I've never thought it was wrong to focus on an issue, weakness or gap for up to two years to bring it up to standard. Your strengths won't go anywhere. In fact, strengths tend to improve when the whole system is improved.

When it comes to training on intuition, "Trust, but verify."

Time Well Spent

I spend considerable time thinking about how to make my training and my athletes' training better. I urge you to do the same. It's quality time that might be far more meaningful than much of what we do in the gym each day.

The Five Jackasses of Fitness

1. The Armchair Quarterback

There is a way of speaking that drives me crazy and it usually starts something like this:

"I'm not sure who's coaching (insert famous name or team), but if I were doing it, we'd (insert a level of success much higher than the current level of success)."

The advice is consistent to what that person does with every client in his corner of the strength training world. And, here's the funny thing: he's probably right!

LeBron's power clean would go through the roof with his kind of strength training. Kobe's plank would improve exponentially and Usain would easily have more range of movement in his shoulder. Too bad performance in their respective sports would take a big hit.

It's the single hardest lesson of being a strength coach—I can make you stronger, but it might not help at all. In fact, it might just hurt, which is captured by the old chestnut, "Looks like Tarzan, plays like Jane."

You might have the fast forty, the big bench and the six-pack abs, but you can't take getting punched in the mouth. You, of course, have to punch back.

I hear this all the time: "If I coached the high school team, we would do CrossFit and out-condition the opposition."

Yeah, yeah, yeah. Well, I actually tried it and it was an epic failure…and I apologize!

"We need to get everybody bigger and stronger."

I tried that, too, and watched my own efforts come back to mock me.

Sometimes, and this is the honest truth, elite athletes are just struggling to survive week to week. Usually if something else would work, they'd already be doing it.

2. The Critic Who Never Lends a Hand

I learned weightlifting from 1965 to 1971 from watching my brothers and from reading what Bruce Randall recommended in the little pamphlet that came with our weightlifting bar. Three sets of ten in a variety of presses, some rows, curls and squatting on the toes to "build your thighs" were all anyone needed.

Then, in 1971, I graduated from the eighth grade and moved on to Southwood Junior High. There we were taught this program:

Power clean: 8, 6, 4
Military press: 8, 6, 4
Front squat: 8, 6, 4
Bench press: 8, 6, 4

My classmates and I ended up doing a lot of those movements that year. However, whenever I write an article about power cleans and front squats, I get twenty questions asking, "What are those lifts?" They shouldn't be that hard to grasp. After all, a group of smelly ninth-graders mastered them perfectly fine.

After leaving high school, I met Dick Notmeyer and for the next few years, I learned the Olympic lifts under his guidance. Five days a week, we went to his gym and trained three hours a day. He charged twenty-five cents a week for dues, though, so obviously he was in it for the money.

But where do most of today's gym rats learn the lifts? Online videos? The majority are pure crap. They're not just wrong, but dangerously wrong. And following the advice of that TV expert doing the kettlebell swing will downright hurt you.

So, do you go to the magazines? The advice is almost universally about combining isolation work. Why not just do some compound movements (power clean, military press, front squat and bench press, for example), increase the load and save time?

Actually, I know why: most people don't know how to do these movements.

I figure it took me fifteen years in the weightroom to start to really understand the basic principles of training. It took even longer to appreciate how to help others.

That's why you either need to stop making fun of the guy curling in the squat rack or go out of your way to help. When I was coming up, most of us learned from the others in the gym. It takes time to learn the ways around the gym, the rack and the platform.

It's time to bring back that "quaint" old habit of helping others.

3. The Anal-Retentive Dieter

Marc Halpern is a registered dietician who trains at my morning sessions. Marc "fixed" my third issue a few months ago, which is the war raging between the various diets.

I recently visited a used bookstore and came away with a great insight. Basically, take any macronutrient and argue "No" or "Only," and then write a book. Years from now, it'll sit on the racks of a used bookstore clashing with the diet books on either side of it. The book that tells us bread is the issue sits next to the Bread Eater's Diet.

In fact, all diets, all methods of caloric restriction and good food selection, will work. You know what I'm going to say.

"Pick one."

Then, stick to it.

Marc gave me that great insight—all diets tend to argue the same facts. If you took a massive Venn diagram and found where they all agree, you'd come away with these conclusions:

- Eat colorful vegetables.
- Avoid cheap sources of carbohydrates (usually from a bag or a box).
- Avoid fats made in a lab. Butter comes from cows, olive oil from olives, but extracting oil from corn takes a lab.

There you go. Sound, solid advice.

Marc then took me a step further. He said to look at nutrition like an arrow. At the base of the arrow is candy, junk food and let's just say pizza as representing fast food.

At the point of the arrow is perfection, and none of us will attain that for very long. Three-quarters up toward the point of the arrow should be veggies, fish, eggs and fruit.

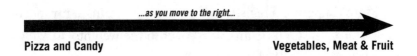

...as you move to the right...

Pizza and Candy   **Vegetables, Meat & Fruit**

Strive for "pretty good" when it comes to diet, and forget perfection. Push your food choices more toward eggs and veggies as opposed to fast food and candy.

Then, stick to it.

4. The Prehab, Mobility, Warmup Wimp

Apparently, all of you are injured, destroyed and depleted. Please, toughen up.

Recently at a gym in San Francisco, I noticed that everyone around me was foam rolling, aligning their chi or doing any one of a number of misguided therapies. They all seemed normal looking to me, but none of them trained. They were all doing various stretchy, rubby things.

Listen, I know there's a time and place for therapy, but you also have to train. Delayed onset muscle soreness isn't a terminal condition. All you need is a little warmup and another training day.

For years, the warmup period has continued to increase in time and fluff until the workout has all but disappeared. Today, many people don't have time to train, as their corrective work takes the bulk of time.

It's the same issue I have with "hydrating." Stop calling it that. It's just drinking water, and my dog does it when he runs after his ball for half an hour.

Intelligent training focusing on the fundamental human movements will be far more effective for joint mobility and lean body mass than all the other crap you find yourself doing.

If you have a specific, fixable issue, by all means fix it. If it needs surgery, schedule that and make sure you have some home care.

Otherwise, stand up and walk over to the weights.

5. The Anonymous Douche

When you post online, use your real name. If you don't want your boss or your mom to read it, don't post it.

It's like these Rambos who come out of the ether to post whenever a killing spree takes place. Invariably, they say something like, "Yeah, he was lucky I wasn't there, cuz I woulda grabbed that rifle and shoved it up his ass and fired until it went click, click, click."

Really? That's what would have happened?

Likewise, I'll post an article and someone will type something like, "Yeah, I just did the 10,000 swings with the 24kg kettlebell and the workout was great."

Or we'll see, "Yeah, I just back-squatted 500 pounds for fifty reps…good workout."

Right. I believe you!

Some day, I hope to visit Gotham City for real and see all these superheroes in person.

A Better Way

1. Understand that coaching real athletes might be tougher than you think. If that interests you, dig deeper, study more, get mentored and learn what it really takes to make athletes better. You'll be surprised and humbled.
2. Criticize less, help more. It'll make you a better person.
3. Choose good foods and don't get too caught up in the diet wars. You probably already know exactly what you need to do to clean up your diet.
4. Don't forget to lift weights when you go to the gym. A twelve-ounce foam roller doesn't count.
5. Do yourself a favor and be "you" online. Anonymity plus audience often equals asshole. Try not to be one. Make Mom proud.

Reasonableness as a Standard

WHEN I MAJORED IN paralegal research at Skyline Junior College, my days were filled with the great canon of Western Civilization and long classes on business and criminal law. The two fields intertwined nearly every day. After discussing the ideals of Classic Greeks, I'd grab my bag, walk down the hall and hear about the basic legal standard.

To understand the law, you must, first and foremost, understand "reasonable" and "reasonableness."

I have always thought this definition of the reasonable person by Percy Henry Winfield to be, well, reasonable:

> *He has not the courage of Achilles, the wisdom of Ulysses or the strength of Hercules, nor has he the prophetic vision of a clairvoyant. He will not anticipate folly in all its forms but he never puts out of consideration the teachings of experience shows such negligence to be common. He is a reasonable man but not a perfect citizen, nor a "paragon of circumspection."*

This sounds like a lot of people I know.

Reasonableness is not only a pillar in the study of law, but it's also considered one of the rocks of a person of integrity.

Integrity, according to my mom, is being one person all the time no matter what the circumstances. I've been with Cardinals of the Catholic Church at dinner, stars from Broadway, professional athletes, Olympians and fitness models, yet I strive to follow this advice from my mother. Ideally, at my funeral, you will all be talking about the same guy in my urn or casket.

Integrity comes from the same root as integer. Like a whole number, integrity asks you to be a whole person. I've found (and this is nothing unusual, as billions have done it before) that being reasonable in our thoughts, actions, beliefs and approach to life allows us to handle the contradictions, disparities and unpleasantness of living in community.

My old college coach, Ralph Maughan, had a sign on his desk:

"Be Reasonable. Do it my way."

Coach Maughan, who was drafted by the Detroit Lions, made an Olympic team as a hammer thrower, won the nationals in the javelin and earned three medals at the Battle of the Bulge, had more reasons to be reasonable, frankly. Coach Maughan, part of the Greatest Generation, had seen and done things that were glorious and tragic, and he understood life well. "His way" was usually a pretty good idea.

As Earl Nightingale tells us in *Lead the Field,* the audiotape series I mentioned that changed my life:

> *And, to me, reasonableness is another word for integrity: integrity to truth, to the evidence, no matter where it leads…Are you ready to discover "through experiment and reflection what course of life will*

fulfill those powers most completely?" That's being true to yourself; that's integrity; that's reasonableness.

"To the evidence, no matter where it leads" is the drumbeat of my search for better ways to seek and attain our goals in fitness, health and sports.

This point is the cornerstone of my talks as we see the question: "Well, where do we get this evidence?"

For me, I've been lucky to have great mentors throughout my career, starting with my brothers. I was also smart enough to trust to just follow what the best were doing and, like I often say, "Do This!"

I've discussed the importance of trusting your own experience, and you'll surely see me ranting about that again soon. I'm also a huge fan of REAL science in the field of fitness, strength and health.

Before I give accolades, let me tell you what I hate in the field of fitness, strength and health: getting a bunch of untrained people to test a strength program or using hung-over college freshmen to prove your program, or testing something under thirteen weeks and pretending it works for every situation and everyone.

I often discuss the pioneering work of Drs. Thomas DeLorme and Arthur Watkins working with both polio patients and the injured soldiers of WWII. In 1945, DeLorme wrote a paper *Restoration of Muscle Power by Heavy-Resistance Exercises*, and published in *The Journal of Bone and Joint Surgery.*

In 300 cases, he found "splendid response in muscle hypertrophy and power, together with symptomatic relief," by following this method of seven to ten sets of ten reps per set for a total of seventy to a hundred repetitions each workout. The weight started off light for the first set and then got progressively heavier until a ten-rep-max (10RM) load was achieved. Over time, things changed in terms of volume. By 1948 and 1951, the authors noted:

> *"Further experience has shown this figure to be too high and that in most cases a total of 20 to 30 repetitions is far more satisfactory. Fewer repetitions permit exercise with heavier muscle loads, thereby yielding greater and more rapid muscle hypertrophy."*

A series of articles and books followed where they recommended three sets of ten reps using a progressively heavier weight in the following manner:

> *Set #1—50% of 10-repetition maximum*
> *Set #2—75% of 10-repetition maximum*
> *Set #3—100% of 10-repetition maximum*

In this scheme, only the last set is performed to the limit. The first two sets can be considered warmups. In their 1951 book, *Progressive Resistance Exercise,* DeLorme and Watkins state:

> *"By advocating three sets of exercise of ten repetitions per set, the likelihood that other combinations might be just as effective is not overlooked...Incredible as it may seem, many athletes have developed great power and yet have never employed more than five repetitions in a single exercise."*

I love that last line.
It's easy to miss their audience: injured vets and polio victims.

My mother of Blessed Memory, Aileen Barbara McCloskey John, feared little in her life. She grew up very poor and then things got worse with the depression. Nearly every man in her life fought in various wars and, admittedly, I did see her cry every day when her sons were in Vietnam. But nothing frightened her like polio did. Polio was the scourge of youth and destroyer of lives for generations. The causes were thought to be swimming pools, ice cream and open windows.

Then, literally overnight, with a series of vaccines the curse ended.

Modern weightlifting's ability to help victims of this disease regain the use of limbs allowed the barbell to become more mainstream in the eyes of many people. DeLorme and Watkins give us a template for reasonable.

My two experiments with Nautilus and CrossFit were, in part, because they seemed so reasonable at that time. The Nautilus facility here in Salt Lake City was within walking distance of my apartment, where I could get a life-affirming, hard workout in well under an hour. As a young teacher with four academic preps, I had little free time. (For non-teachers: I was teaching at a college prep school, and nightly I had to prepare for four lectures from Ancient Civ and Western Civ to Modern American History and Economics…a broad range).

I made great physical progress for a few months and then stalled out.

I consulted Ellington Darden by telephone a few times, and he convinced me to do less and less. I have often mentioned that it was his passing comment, "Play some chess," that encouraged me to become the school's chess coach, something I still recommend for young football coaches.

But the Nautilus style of training soon stagnates and, as a thrower, it was impossible not to see the fact that my distances were suffering. Returning to the platform, I added a few Olympic lifts and soon was back on track (lousy attempt at track and field humor).

My first exposure to CrossFit was the same: when I first came on the internet, both Tamir Katz and Robb Wolf asked me to launch a website to counter the HIT Jedis.

It's odd to think of this now, but the early internet fitness sites were limited to mostly High Intensity Training people (HIT Jedis was the term they used for themselves) and Atkins Diet webchains. I would almost have to sit down and explain things to many of you about the web in 1998: it wasn't the same as it is today. Back then most of the sites had exploding hearts and tumbling kitty GIFs and not much else.

When I first heard about CrossFit, I still had my softhome.net email address, which, sadly, I can't access now, but you can read what I was reading at the CrossFit archives.

One thing that hit me is the lack of swimming in the past few years on the main CrossFit site. I asked Greg Glassman about this a decade ago, and he told me that whenever he posted a swimming workout, he'd get email questions about substitutions, so he dropped swimming completely.

Things have changed…I just can't imagine emailing CrossFit now about a scaling question or an exercise substitution and getting a response back from Greg. Although one can argue about those archives and doing max pullups right after max bench presses—that was the combo that blew my friend's shoulder… Jerry or "9–7" as everyone calls him—but, honestly, at the time most of the workouts were reasonable and doable.

A young man got hurt recently in a CrossFit competition, because what was expected simply wasn't reasonable. Percy Henry Winfield, and many jurors, would agree.

"To the evidence, no matter where it leads" will continue to be my framework in designing training.

The longer I play in this game, the more I become convinced that what Coach Maughan told me about training is the truth of what we do:

"Little and often, over the long haul."

I've been lifting since 1965, coaching since 1979, and am just beginning to understand what "the long haul" means.

Training Clarity: One Goal at a Time

CLARITY IS AN ISSUE in the strength training field.

I could yell, "Ace, LeRoy, Middle Stretch" and eleven freshman football players would all know where to line up, block, run, move and attack as soon as the ball was snapped.

But when I say, "Squatting is important," I get questions about high bar, low bar, Zercher, goblet, box, front, overhead, Smith machine and probably a dozen other styles, options and nuances I've yet to learn.

Part of the issue with strength and conditioning is that we have a set of tools. It doesn't matter how long your list is, whether it includes barbells, machines, kettlebells, dumbbells or whatever, there seems to be some confusion about the application of these tools to "this."

What is "this"?

It's qualities.

The basic barbell is unmatched for building strength. The Olympic lifting moves—including the military press that left competition in 1972, but is still a good idea for anyone—can change lives. You can build a level of strength that can stop your older brother's friend from ever talking bad about you again.

I witnessed this with my friend Eric.

One of my most cherished memories is telling Eric, "You can let him down now." Eric had push-pressed an older, mouthy friend of his brother up into the air and, to be honest, it was fun to watch his feet dangle for a few bit.

If you want even more satisfaction, the three powerlifts (bench, squat and deadlift) are unrivaled in their ability to change 97-pound weaklings into monsters who belch thunder and fart lightning.

What about mobility and flexibility?

As early as 1980, I wrote that the overhead squat, straight-leg deadlift, dip and pullup (done correctly) could do more for flexibility than all the ballet classes at charm school.

If you need proof, teach a correct front squat to someone off the street. Sure, strength will be an issue, but more likely the problem will be flexibility of the wrists, elbows, shoulders, back and legs. Other than those joints and a few others, front squats require no mobility or flexibility at all. (For those missing the gene, that was sarcasm.)

For hypertrophy, a.k.a. bodybuilding, the barbell is still the tool of choice. Although I put on forty pounds of mass in four months doing nothing but the O lifts, I can't ignore the contributions of the generations of lifters who used the barbell for bodybuilding. I maintain the advice the great Robbie Robinson gave me years ago—to mix front squats with straight-leg deadlifts and bench presses and pullups for hypertrophy—stands the test of time.

And finally, for this odd thing I call "Armor Building," I maintain that quality fighters need to deal with contact, snatch-grip deadlifts, Zercher squats, biceps curls (especially with a thick bar) and bench presses. That protocol will answer the call better than anything else.

One tool—the barbell—answers the question for a number of qualities, like strength, mobility, flexibility, hypertrophy and general toughening. The problem is, when most people go to the gym to train, they strive to do literally everything at once.

There's also another issue: most of us can't help but think that unless we're putting the pedal to the metal, going right into the red zone and then hitting the wall, we aren't truly training.

To sum the issue:

We have one tool (or several, but weights are weights).

We have one mindset.

This is the problem.

Before I get too far, it's true that a new lifter can do just about anything. Hypertrophy, strength, power and mobility will all improve when we go from zero to something.

Linear progression is about the greatest and most wonderful part of training. The first time I was taught the snatch, I made 165 pounds. Three weeks later, I was bigger and snatched 187, then 209 in my next meet.

In nine months, I improved from that original 165 to 231 pounds. Sixteen years later, I did my lifetime best of 314 pounds. If you were born the first day I Olympic lifted, you could drive to the meet the day I set my personal record.

However, it wasn't linear after those first nine months.

Once you get off that initial wonderful ride as a beginner, you need to start using a new toolkit. It's difficult to try to do everything all the time. This is where we need good coaching or a mentor or just some basic logic.

I'd like you to consider two simple ways of looking at your training that might direct you to taking on one quality at a time (or at most two) and bringing yourself to a goal reasonably quickly.

First, the calendar is the single greatest training tool you have for success. The training diary and the food journal are also absolutely necessary, but those tools tell the history.

I ate this...

I lifted that...

The calendar is proactive. The calendar gives ideas about where you want to go and a bit of a roadmap to this destination.

The first idea is based on the traffic light. This works well for some people. The problem is that while green means "go," the other two colors have a few issues.

Green works because during the months you highlight as green months, you can focus on challenges and programs that demand focus, drive and intensity. If you need to toss down some tablets or extra caffeine to do the 21-Day Challenge or whatever, do it. It's not a lifetime commitment!

If you want to build mass, I have a plan in my book *Mass Made Simple*. It's six weeks, fourteen workouts and a ton of reps. For O lifters, I have the Big 21 program, which just plain sucks during the third week. But for three or six weeks, you can pound through the pain.

Yellow is the problem. On traffic lights, it means caution, but we use the color to refer to those "punch the clock" workouts that people who've been around a while understand very well.

Most trainees miss this opportunity to understand that there are times, perhaps long stretches, where you need to get your workouts finished, eat fairly clean, and take care of basic recovery.

During the green-light, crazy training, you can afford to use a lot of energy trying to dial in perfection, but I've yet to find someone who can do this longer than six weeks without support from a government body, a wealthy spouse or anabolics.

Red, of course, means stop. I used to think divorce would be a red-light training time, but also I've met women who use training as a means to attack the demons.

Surgeries, life-altering problems and a few other things are red-light periods. I'd still argue to move, eat well and check your recovery, but I also understand how difficult even minimal training can be in certain situations.

The red, yellow and green light system provides us a basic tool to say "maybe not now."

The impact on training is obvious. You can attack your training when you're in green. Red and yellow situations don't mean you have to toss out your training, exercise or supplement regimes. In fact, this is the time where a workout might be supportive of the your issues.

It is not, however, the time to ratchet up the volume, intensity or load.

I'm working on teaching people to be more proactive about this so they can focus certain periods of the year on the reality of their lives.

For example, a tax accountant should cross out March and April on the calendar as obvious "yellow light months." A teacher could maybe do the same for May and June, and August and September. Certainly, it wouldn't be a bad idea for parents of younger children to put December into an "X" with all the concerts, pageants, plays and stuff.

The minutes you spend each year looking at when to ramp up your training and when you want to simply show up is like playing with house money. You can't lose.

Another way to look at a year-round approach to reasonable training is the "bus bench" and "park bench" workouts.

Bus bench workouts: You're expecting results—on time, like you're hoping the bus will be!

Park bench workouts are an opportunity to explore and enjoy where you are in your training.

It's a simple concept. Like weights, benches have multiple uses. If you're waiting to get to work sitting on a bus bench, you don't just hope, you demand that the bus be on time. If it's even a little late, it could ruin your day at work.

Park benches are built the same way, but when you sit in a park, you don't expect or worry if Toby the squirrel comes by or not. You sit back and enjoy the process.

My co-writer of *Fat Loss Happens on Monday*, Josh Hillis, believes that almost universally, people need four months of bus-bench training each year, split into two-month periods—two two-month blocks of focused training a year.

The rest of the year should be park-bench workouts where the training goals are simply to train. You could cross out eight months a year and still follow a plan that could achieve just about any goal.

This is contrary to what most people think. There's this idea that constant exhausting training is the only path to the goal. It's not true—and it's destroying many people's journey to their goals.

What's a bus-bench program? Well, as a graduate of the Velocity Diet—twenty-eight days of basically no food, just six low-carb shakes a day—I would've punched Chris Shugart right in the mouth (in a kind, caring way) if it hadn't sliced up my abs.

This is the epitome of the bus-bench workouts: you expect, even demand results. You can learn a lot more about the park bench and bus bench concept in my book called *Intervention*.

I did a program called Kettlebell Fever over four weeks, and one of the first week's workouts included 245 squats and 315 swings. The author should be very happy that I had excellent results.

Mass-building programs and fat-cutting programs are the poster children for bus-bench workouts. Sadly, that's also the problem, as most people shuffle from one new ebook or diet or fat-loss secret to another in a blind stumble.

You have to attack fat loss as an all-out war with every resource at your command. That's hard to do for 365 days in a row.

For mass building, there's no question that high-rep squatting piles on muscle. I went back through my volumes of journals, and I've never been able to do high-rep squatting beyond six weeks before the wheels literally came off. Oh, I got big and lost a bunch of fat, but my joints just said, "Enough!"

Once or twice a year, make mass building your goal, and give it everything you have.

Look at your calendar and the events you have coming up and decide when you're going to bring all your weapons to bear.

I make my living on park-bench workouts. I spend a lot of time talking people off the ledge who think every workout, every day, every year, should be defending Sparta against the Persians.

I'm a strong believer that, for the bulk of your time you need to just be sure to take care of the basics.

The basics?

Well, first are you doing the basic human movements?

- Push
- Pull
- Hinge
- Squat
- Loaded carries

If you're doing the basic movements at least once a week, are your reps and loads appropriate?

It's not that complex, as most programs tend to gravitate around that magic fifteen-to-twenty-five number like:

- 3 sets of 5
- 5 sets of 3
- 3 sets of 8
- 5 sets of 5

Keep adding plates when appropriate, and just continue to get to the gym and take care of business.

Pavel Tsatsouline handed me a great two-day-a-week training program that I shared with a young, busy guy who told me it was too easy. I knew he was lying, so I tweaked it for him. Here's the King of Less Training Program.

Day One	Day Two
Bench press	Bench press
Squat	Deadlift

Now, let's look at my tweaks:

- Only 45 and 25-pound plates.
- No less than ten reps on every set of bench and squat until the last set.
- No less than five reps on every deadlift.
- So, the bench press workout was sets of ten, add weight until the last set, where you grind out as many as possible.

Here's a bench example from 1993 when I did this basic program:

135 × 10
225 × 10
315 × 10
365 × "as many"

For the squat, the last set should be around bodyweight, usually 185 or 225, and you go for at least thirty reps.

In the deadlift, keep grinding out those sets of five. Over time, feel free to slide this down to three reps, then two reps.

I've suggested other minimalistic programs, and other authors have done a much better job than me. The important thing is to get to the gym and train your whole body with an appropriate load, and then go home.

The point is, we have tools to train strength, fat loss, hypertrophy, mobility and power: the barbell and all the other friends and family of iron.

Sadly, it's nearly impossible to work all those qualities all the time. Actually, it's impossible.

We need to have the courage to mark certain periods of the year when we'll ratchet up the intensity and go after it. Two of those qualities, hypertrophy and fat loss, only seem to work well in tight focused "all in" programs anyway.

For most of your year, train intelligently and get your reps and sets in. Oddly, I've discovered that these are the times where strength improves almost miraculously. I don't know why, but that's how it works.

Keep training and food journals, but invest in a calendar and think about your life and when you can really go after it.

If you're too cheap to buy a calendar, the local mortuary gives them away for free. It's the best investment I know.

Eat Like a Warrior King

THERE ARE GREAT LESSONS to be learned from the great heroes of literature. For one thing, they can teach us how to eat to build muscle, lose fat and crush the competition.

Don't believe me? Then you haven't read *Beowulf* in a while.

In the story of *Beowulf,* warriors speak purely in the present. They mention the past in passing and rarely look beyond the next fight. Kings, however, speak differently. They first review history, then they sum up the present and give us a hopeful look ahead.

In short, warriors live in the present while kings live in a world where they need to look backward as well as forward to assess what to do next.

Now, I'm a coach, not a king.

But I've gathered a little wisdom during my four decades of under-the-bar experience. For example, I've noticed that many strength and fitness athletes tend to look at food like a warrior: here it is, I eat it. Sometimes that's exactly what you need. Other times, it's better to look upon food as a king in *Beowulf.*

Let's start by reexamining our relationship with food.

Warrior Eating

First, let's look at a warrior approach to food.

Initially, I thought about doing the Velocity Diet. I "thought" about it, but it sounded too painful. Then I performed badly in several Highland Games and at a major track meet. Literally, in a hotel room in Pleasanton, California, something deep inside me called out, "Velocity Diet!"

After the V-Diet, I broke a state record in the snatch.

Folks, the V-Diet is warrior all the way. It's all in. There's no moderation there.

As I've written before, fat loss is an all-out war. With the V-Diet you attack bodyfat for four weeks with everything you have. It's not a lifestyle choice; it's a battle. Moderation is for losers, at least for twenty-eight days.

The V-Diet is Warrior 101. A dozen or so bottles of protein, a blender and some supplements is all you need for the next few weeks. When someone asks, "Is it good for you?" you reply, "Have you seen my abs?!"

In other words, for fat loss, the winning approach is living in the pure present: be a warrior.

Moms Versus Warriors

About five years ago, I had the opportunity at a military workshop to work with some people who were doing a form of intermittent fasting.

Due to the location, we could only find one place still open for dinner, a popular fast food place with a red and gold clown as a salesperson. These five guys hadn't eaten all day, and I'm sure every mother and father in the place shielded their children's eyes from the spectacle that took place.

It was a sight to behold as burger after burger was flushed down. As one guy explained, "I only eat once; I have to eat a lot." For the record, these guys were all ripped and in great physical condition. It may have been frightening to the observers, but it worked for them.

That's the warrior mentality. Look at what you see here:

- There isn't a lot of cooking in any of these examples.
- This isn't the way your mom told you to eat.

No, the warrior way probably involves a number of things Mom doesn't want you to do. But let's make this clear: for fat loss and short-term goals, I'm convinced nothing works better than the warrior approach.

Getting ripped, truly lean, isn't about taste buds, satiety or gourmet cooking. It's about using food as a tool, and dealing with hunger. And I believe you can do it for short periods throughout your life.

Eat Like a (Grown-up) King

For all other goals and any kind of lifetime approach, I recommend following the kingly way—have a long-term focus.

Someone recently asked me for the secret to nutrition. Seriously, you don't know what to do about food? Here's an idea: eat like an adult.

I'll say it again: Grow up.

It reminds me of what they tell students at top universities: "Look to your right. Now, look to your left. Every person around you was a straight-A student in high school, the class president and valedictorian. Get over it."

Every success in your life doesn't call for several extra rounds of beer, a salutary doughnut and high fives from everyone. You're an adult now; you don't need a cookie every time you do something special.

Great athletes score a touchdown, goal or point and just keep moving along. It's your job, so get over it.

If you want to look good in the future, you have to start looking at food like, well, food and not a reward.

Step one to the kingly approach to eating is to have a long-term focus. We all know that vegetables, lean protein and fresh water are the best choices meal-in and meal-out the rest of our lives. If you hover around those choices for the bulk of your meals, you'll be fine.

You know this. Do this.

The next issue with the kingly approach is cooking. You should do it. Mommy can't always be there for you. I offer two classic strength-training cooking methods: grilling and crock pot.

It was funny to have dinner at Mark Rippetoe's house. When I got there, Mark began by showing me some twigs. "Usually, this time of year I go with pinion, as you can foul up with the mesquite."

I believe that's what he had said, but what really struck me was the effort—the love—that Mark was putting into his grilling.

In the strength world, there are many extraordinarily strong men who are also brilliant cooks. In Dallas, the best barbeque I ever had was at a shot putter's place.

The point here is important: big ribs, chickens, beef and pork prepared well and eaten a lot seems to make a person big and strong.

Now, I know some of my readers prefer tofu with sprouts and you are, I'm sure, beloved by the universe. But, and I am saying this nicely, big iron demands the big meals.

My favorite breakfast is crack oatmeal. We call it that because it's addicting. Check it out:

Crack Oatmeal

Ingredients

- Real oatmeal, not instant, about two inches of it in the bottom of the slow cooker.
- Raisins. A lot.
- Cinnamon, both the ground kind and a stick or two.
- Any kind of fruit, dried or fresh, you have handy. Throw it in.
- A little bit of vanilla. This will give it a smell that makes you want more and more.
- Chia seeds, a few spoonfuls.
- Water, milk, or cream to cover the dry stuff. Stir once.

Put this on low for about three hours. Then, turn the slow cooker off and add some protein powder, a couple of scoops, and some extra water, milk or cream. Make sure it's a little soft and soggy. It'll continue to thicken over time. The raisins will really plump up, too, indicating you're on the right track.

Let it sit overnight. Upon rising, crank it up to hot for about ten minutes and mix it up nice.

Need dinner now? Try this:

One-Pan Stew

Ingredients

- Olive oil
- Stew meat (a pound or two)
- Frozen stew vegetables
- A can of tomato soup
- A can of French onion soup (the secret ingredient)

First, add the oil to a big pan and brown the meat. Then, add all the other stuff. Stir to a gentle boil, cover and wait about five minutes. That's it. It's very good.

Finally, to eat like a king, you need to shop like a king. Take one day per week, maybe Sunday, to shop and prepare meals. Sunday and Wednesday cooking days will definitely have you covered.

That's a kingly approach to food. And it seems to give the best results for fat loss that stays off.

Warrior King

The warrior approach to food is absolutely correct—sometimes. When you need to zero in on fat loss or another equally focused goal, I can't think of a better idea than the Velocity Diet or another choice that basically divorces nutrition from thought. It's a meal. Eat it. Deal with it.

For the bulk of our lives, however, I suggest developing a kingly relationship with food in which you plan, prepare and consume with a vision of satiety, leanness, fullness and long-term success.

You know, eat like an adult.

But keep the warrior mentality handy.

Get Your Push Back

I DO A LOT OF CONSULTATIONS on the telephone. It's still the best way I know to get a sense of what people are doing and, maybe more important, what they think they're doing.

Writing emails, letters, and articles has lead me to an inescapable conclusion: most trainees understand only about ten percent of what they read. This might explain why a friend of mine did benches and curls on his "leg day."

When I first talk to someone, I ask about the background in training. With a rare exception, the following is the first statement:

"My best bench is…"

After hearing literally dozens of people sum up their training with a bench press number, I began to think that of all the basic human movements—push, pull, hinge, squat, and loaded carry—the last thing you should worry about is the push.

But then, my clientele got more special.

Big, Banged-Up Bob

I began working with a guy we'll call "Bob." Bob is 6' 8" and weighs 310 pounds. He's only this light in the off-season and will bulk up nicely for his job as an NFL lineman.

He makes a fair amount of money stopping people from hitting quarterbacks, and he's done the job well enough to wear three Super Bowl rings. He has a few issues, of course: he can't straighten out his left arm and his right shoulder is a mess.

He's not the only one. I've been working with several elite athletes the past few years who just can't push as well as a normal person. Because of these people, I've developed a little system for bringing the push back to the game.

Enter the Pushup Plank

As always, I start with patterning. In the world of pushes, I think the plank is the base.

Oh, and I also know this: nobody I know thinks they need planks. But I have a little test I stole from Stuart McGill, the great back expert from Canada:

"If you can't hold a plank for two minutes either you're obese or your abdominal training is wrong."

Not flawed, mind you, wrong!

Keep in mind, though, what Gray Cook talks about, too: you can do a side plank for the month of June and still fall apart when you move. Make sure you consider mobility, too.

I use the pushup-position plank (PUPP) for most people. This is a plank performed by holding the top of a pushup, arms extended. A beat-up athlete can almost always still PUPP, and you can easily blend the exercise with other movements. It's a great rest exercise to make an easy workout harder.

I like to mix swings and goblet squats with PUPPs. It's simple: instead of resting between exercises, plank between exercises.

Now, here's the key: it's getting up and down off the ground that will drive the heart rate through the roof, not the actual plank.

I use every plank imaginable. And I quickly work everyone into doing wall-assisted handstands, too. Once I accomplish this, I move to the King of Planks: the cartwheel.

The Cartwheel. (Really.)

Yes, I know, no one does cartwheels, but when I first read Ken Shamrock's training programs and saw his use of cartwheels, I was impressed so I tried them. It was one of the most difficult conditioning workouts of my life! In addition, my shoulders were given a workout that shocked me.

It's a rare person who wouldn't gain from more planks in their training. Use planks as a focused rest period by mixing them with a big move, or add some cartwheels into your outdoor conditioning. It will shock you, too.

The issue I always deal with is this: there's some belief that the plank, or any patterning exercise for that matter, is beginner stuff and not worthy of an elite.

Hey, we're all beginners when it comes to the quality of movement.

Military + Bench = Win

The grind family is pretty obvious in the push world: pushups, bench press, military press and, literally, the list seems endless. I'm a big believer in both military and bench press for nearly every athlete I train. I've been doing both since 1971 and I've kept my shoulders reasonably healthy by keeping both in my weekly training quiver.

For most people, the grinding presses are about all that will be needed. I honestly wish I could say more, but there are far better people to speak on the press than me. As you know, I'm a big fan of Jim Wendler's 5/3/1 training. He advocates both presses each week, so I'm in good company.

Symmetry Press Workouts

This is the step that most people skip. But anyone who wants to hit or throw at high speeds needs to consider these: symmetry press workouts.

I was first exposed to the one-arm bench press by the late Lane Cannon. We did them in his basement, and there I discovered that my body is "one piece."

When I recommend them, I always note to keep the free, non-weighted hand "free." Don't grab onto anything; just let the hand stay free. This will demand that your body lock up and become solid. The one-arm bench press will be one of the greatest ab workouts of your life.

Ethan Reeve filled in the next part of the equation for me, the one-arm standard. He believes hoisting 125 pounds for five reps on the one-arm bench press is the gold standard for his athletes. I lowered this to seventy pounds for five reps for our high school boys.

Prepare yourself before you jump up and try this challenge. With anything around 100 pounds, the weight will really pull your off-side around and down the bench. You have to counter it by aggressively squeezing everything from your feet up in order to deal with the weight. It's a full body lift with heavy weights. Remember: keep the off-arm free!

Here's the deal: If you can do 125 pounds with the right and only seventy with the left, you have an issue.

Now, I don't know what that issue is, but it's better to deal with it with one-arm work than to do what often happens: add explosiveness to an asymmetrical issue.

It's far better to deal with this problem in a systematic approach that includes strengthening the weak side, addressing mobility and flexibility issues and perhaps even doing some aggressive rehab work.

The One-Arm Overhead Press

Fifteen years ago, it was rare to see anyone one-arm overhead press. With the influence of the kettlebell, the lift has returned with a vengeance.

I'm a big fan of this lift, and many of my personal workouts are anchored with one-arm presses. Again, it's easy to see asymmetries here. I'd suggest that most men strive for a half-bodyweight one-arm overhead press and, logically, be able to do it with each hand.

Most people find that their one-arm presses combined are heavier than their two-hand barbell press overhead. It makes some sense as you have two legs and your whole body supporting the single-arm press, and most people don't have four legs and two torsos!

If you have symmetry, by all means move up to the push press or other explosive moves. Someone not long ago asked me why people get bigger when they do push presses. My answer, obviously genius, was this: "Because you use bigger weights."

There's a truth in that statement that most skinny trainees never grasp. *Bigger Faster Stronger* has a video of me push pressing 365 for five reps. At that load, you must have a fairly solid foundation underneath the bar.

The push press is simple: With the weight on the chest, the normal position for overhead pressing, dip your legs in a controlled bend. I used to tell people to do a quarter-squat. Then, vigorously drive the bar using your whole body into the finished press position.

It's relatively easy to do, but take your time adding plates.

There's an issue with your chin being in the way of the bar as you drive it up, and it takes a bit of practice to learn to pull your chin out of the way. I learned that the hard way.

Beyond the Bench

The press is a favorite for most lifters, but there's still a need to look at the push through the lens of patterning, grinding, and symmetry.

There are few things more rewarding than holding a big lift overhead or nailing a big number in the bench press. Long-term improvement can come from including some work with planks and one-arm presses, in addition to the countless sets of bench presses.

Your shoulders will thank me.

Six Challenges You Must Accept and Beat

PART OF THE PROBLEM WITH THE modern internet warrior who claims a 750-pound deadlift and a bodyfat percentage of four percent is that he's never truly challenged. Many who want to train like a Spec Ops ninja might not even be able to survive basic boot camp training.

Folks, we need challenges. Let's start with the basics and then slide up a bit.

First, let's at least be as strong as a high school football player. Can you bench, front squat and power clean 205? That's become the standard for most schools in the past few years. If you're not yet there, strive to at least meet these metrics:

- A bodyweight bench press
- A bodyweight power clean
- Somewhere in the realm of a double-bodyweight deadlift

But let's take it up a notch. I have a number of challenges I've offered through the years. Some suck and some have no value, but some can change your life.

I have no idea what specific benefits you'll reap from meeting any of these challenges, but I do know this: each of these will make you better at whatever else you do.

1. The Bodyweight Squat Challenge

Load a bar up with your bodyweight. Put it on your shoulders, step back from the rack, and do fifty reps. I did this for the first time in 1976. I was looking for a way to increase my bodyweight and ran it by a friend who responded, "Why not?" Within a few minutes, I would have dozens of answers for "why not?" and none of them were good.

Before we go into detail, though, we'll probably see lots of YouTube videos with guys half-squatting or doing them on a Smith machine and then boasting they've met the challenge. No, they haven't. I'm talking about fifty ass-to-grass back squats with approximately bodyweight propped on your shoulders. Use a barbell, step back from the rack, and have alert spotters really close and enjoy.

If you weigh 135 pounds or less, use 135 pounds. From 135 to 185 pounds, use 185 pounds. If you're in the range of 186–205, use 205. Everyone over 205 should just use 225 pounds. This method will allow you to use a limited number of plates (one or two) and you don't have to experience a lot of clanging and sliding.

The next time you try it, feel free to use whatever load you want, but the experience of doing all fifty is mind blowing.

Not only will you KNOW you had a growth hormone response (they used to tell us that feeling nauseated was a sign that GH was released), but you'll probably never again think that doing just a few sets of squats in a conventional workout is difficult.

2. The Deadlift Challenge

My brother Gary established an interesting challenge you might try once a year. Just as you should with the bodyweight squat for fifty, plan on taking some days off after you attempt this challenge.

It's very simple: How many deadlifts can you do with 315 pounds in half an hour? Time for some caveats—we're assuming your deadlift is well above 315 pounds and we're hoping you have the wisdom to rest, stop, adjust...and possibly quit as appropriate. By the way, Gary did sixty-one reps in the deadlift at 315 in half an hour at age sixty-one.

3. The Snatch Challenge

If you have the courage, I'd like to challenge every reader to snatch bodyweight. The Olympic snatch is often called the "fastest movement in sport" (I don't want to hear the nerd argument about whether or not it's the fastest). It's also technical and, of course, there's that one other thing—you have to be very strong.

When I was in college, the powerlifters at the university always tried making excuses for my lifts. They noted that although I lifted a lot, my ability was "just good technique." Well, it's also being really strong, too. Taking bodyweight from the ground to overhead in one motion is universally recognized as the entry level to the road to being damn strong.

4. The Farmer Walk Challenge

Doing a farmer walk with double bodyweight is a feat worthy of posting on social media. It only has to be a carry for maybe twenty steps or so, but even that's impressive. The problem used to be finding the implements. If you weigh 150 pounds or less, you'll probably find dumbbells to do this. The rest of us, though, might have a harder time.

Enter the trap bar. You'll get all the same effects (working the grip and posterior chain, along with eye-bulging discomfort) that you would from doing it with dumbbells or other implements. Just load it up to twice your bodyweight and stroll away.

5. The Hunger Games Challenge

This one is a dietary challenge. It's simple: once in a while, just don't eat for twenty-four hours. (Don't do this on a workout day.) Eat dinner, and then don't eat anything until dinner the next day. I'm not generally an advocate for intermittent fasting, but many of us in the world of bulk and power need to practice being hungry again. If you're looking for a way to increase your mental focus, this is the "fastest" way I know.

6. The Chill-Out Challenge

There's one final non-lifting challenge I'd like you to consider and that's to take an occasional one-hour timeout from everything. Find a place where you won't be disturbed and turn off everything. No interaction of any kind, no reading, no pacing, nothing. Just sit alone for an hour.

If you must, put a kitchen timer set to buzz in an hour. It might feel like forever, but listen to your "mental traffic." The Age of Exploration was half a millennium ago, but today we live in the Age of Distraction.

Try living without distraction for an hour.

In closing, anything can be a challenge. Those above are time-tested and will give you a chance to discover some gaps.

Foam Rollers Are for Wimps!

"WE DIDN'T DO ENOUGH foam rolling!"

I can guarantee no losing coach from the Super Bowl, Heineken Cup or the Olympics will ever utter that phrase as a reason for not winning.

This started to concern me years ago when I first began to add foam rolling and correctives to my training sessions. I noticed something very troubling—the athletes in the weightroom were conducting themselves with the intensity of middle-aged women waiting for the next yoga class.

Foam rolling isn't the same edge as bodyweight snatches or double-bodyweight squats. Seriously, it just isn't as intense, but do I really have to tell you that?

It's a fine line we walk in strength coaching. Yes, we need to expand our tissue work, our correctives and our quality of movement, but let's be honest here—we've forgotten that we also have to lift some damn weights!

Friends, we have to be able to do both: take care of business on the restorative and corrective side, and on the other side, try to move enough iron so the bar bends a bit.

The Biggest Change

Probably the biggest change in my career in the past few years has been the number of workshops I attend. In the past, I'd catch a clinic about once a year, and perhaps once every few years I'd find myself at a workshop running around, doing drills and making a fool of myself.

Since I'm invited to a lot of workshops now, I try to get there early and listen in. Now, as Laree Draper (publisher at On Target Publications and wife of the great bodybuilder Dave Draper) will attest, I like to sit in the front row. Part of the reason is that I want to be the first—the first to hear it, the first to see it, the first to try it.

It was only recently that I discovered I had a skill, which I'm about to share, that allows me to take in all these new ideas or new equipment and keep the training programs fairly seamless.

I've mentioned the concept before from David Denby's outstanding book *Great Books,* but I think it deserves a deeper study. It's called Think Double.

Thinking Double

As we wade through what seems like a new fad or catchall term each year—with core, functional, thoracic mobility (and all the other adjectives put in front of "mobility"), foam rolling and the use of the word "elite" being the big sinners—it becomes increasingly apparent that while the original idea might have been sound, the hucksters and hawkers have left us wondering if we're going to die if we don't rub out our soft tissues.

This is thinking double. "Thinking double" is a concept I picked up from David Denby's great book, *Great Books.* It says it's perfectly okay to have conflicting thoughts rolling around in your head. There's a lot of sound thinking behind correctives, for example, but no one needs to spend the bulk of their training correcting things that are fine.

It's like the skinny guy in the gym who always does cardio but wants to get bigger—try lifting heavy weights. There's an obviousness about thinking double that many dismiss as, well, obvious.

Foam Rolling and Rolling

The thing I like best about foam rolling is that we have to get on the ground to do it. If I were to underline the biggest gap in most people's training (besides lack of a quality squat and any kind of loaded carries), it would be the total lack of groundwork.

Foam rolling gets people on the ground, and that's a good start. If you want to try an interesting experiment, get a heart rate monitor and for five minutes, get down on the ground (vary the position, front or back or sides) and stand up. Repeat. Yes, that's it. Now check that heart monitor.

Oh, you shouldn't do this in public gyms, as you'll look like you're crazy. We used to do this in high school football when it was called "grass drills." They're also known as "up-downs," and, frankly, this one thing sucked more than every other awful thing associated with playing the game.

However, for middle-aged folks this simple drill, done unloaded, might actually be a lifesaver.

Listen, if you bring peanut butter to a daycare facility, someone will call the SWAT team to take you down. It's nearly criminal to pop open a can of peanut butter on a plane. I'm not sure of the stats on the deaths by peanut butter, but I know this: 28,000 Americans in the fifty-plus age range die yearly in fall-related injuries.

That's stunning.

Lightning kills just over a hundred, and every track and field coach has a full protocol when a bolt is seen. But outside of a few mats and rails, what have you done to train yourself (or your folks or clients) to prepare for something that's about 280 times more likely to happen to you?

Ground Work

So, my groundwork "thinks double." It has a cardio component by popping up and down; it has a tissue aspect (more in a moment); and it has a preventive quality in terms of being less likely to get injured from falling.

On tissue quality, I see two often-overlooked things.

First, I enjoy foam rolling with the best of them. I don't believe the hype about a lot of it, as I've read and listened to long, waxing stories of emptying the lymph nodes and extending the "this" or the "that."

I enjoy my yoga class and I've added a move called "rolling my eyes" when the instructor tells us a position realigns the ascending colon.

But I do think it makes me feel better, and it might lend itself to better training. However, I will say this: if my child was roped down to train tracks and the engine was coming around the mountain, I wouldn't foam roll before I sprinted over to save her.

Second, moving on the ground builds that quality I call "armor building." I've had long talks with Chip Morton, strength coach of the Cincinnati Bengals, about how we as strength coaches can "toughen up" athletes with certain moves.

I literally stumbled across this when one of my running backs noted that doing kettlebell cleans was a lot like the pounding he took running the ball. I thought about how some things, like those damn grass drills, really do mimic what game conditions feel like.

Perhaps grass drills realign the ascending colon.

Regardless, groundwork seems to toughen one up a bit. I've noticed, for example, that when I have to crawl around in my subbasement, just under four feet of height and a huge space, I'm sore in the oddest places the next day. Groundwork preps us for the ups and downs of life.

Literally.

Half-Kneeling Work

Thanks to Brett Jones and Gray Cook, half-kneeling movements are now used in many facilities. If you don't know what they are, it's training on one knee. We look for a ninety-degree angle between the upper and lower legs—make yourself long when you do these. With my trainees, we use the half-kneeling position every workout.

The pelvis is a bowl and the rib cage is like a box. I use a simple example at least weekly where I put a small box on a bowl I have in the gym. If everything is flush and square, the two objects could sit still for millennia. If you tilt the bowl, the box has to adjust.

When you half-kneel, the bowl of the pelvis must be square. To train that we do several things.

First, the big toe of the down foot (if your left knee is on the ground, it would be your right big toes) needs to push into the ground. Focus and feel that the whole time.

Second, actively strive to stretch the front of the straight, down hip. For nearly everyone, the big toe and the stretch the hips cues are enough.

We do basically two exercises daily—press and paddle. With a kettlebell, begin pressing in this half-kneeling position. Use both hands and strive to feel the big toe and the stretch throughout. You shouldn't squirm around too much.

For many, this is the single best way to stretch the front of the hip. If you suddenly become unstable, you lost the box and bowl positions. Realign and begin again.

The paddle idea is the same as Cook's various chops and lifts, but we changed it for our purposes because we don't have a cable machine here. We use the TRX Rip Trainer, but any pulley device will work. A trusted training partner with a rope or towel can work well, too.

With the same left knee down, pull the resistance from high and right, to low and left. This lights up the hip in a way that makes stretching exercises seem like a waste of time (as they often can be).

Again, this is thinking double. We need to stretch the hip flexors, maintain a solid core and press. Janda's research into tonic and phasic muscles forced me to rethink stretching the hip flexors, for example, and developing the deltoids and triceps.

Well, here you go. With half-kneeling work we do both.

Strength Is Corrective

But strength training can be, and absolutely is, corrective. I had a Saturday training session for the greater part of my career based on these moves:

- Overhead squat
- Straight leg deadlift
- Chinups (neck touching the bar)
- Dips
- Side bend of some kind

With my competition schedule, I normally competed on Saturday—Highland Games and track meets. I'd come home from a long day and do these lifts. I continue to believe this group of five movements provided me with not only a tonic, refreshing workout (nothing ballistic, nothing that took a lot of thought), but I was stretched out by the moves.

These movements tended to "put everything back into place." This is a scientific concept, meaning it made me feel whole again. I doubt I ever did more than twenty reps of any of the movements (a few sets of five to eight reps of each) and always walked away feeling better than when I started.

I moved this workout to Sunday many times due to travel or the onset of too many "wee drams" at the Highland Games, but the idea is to use the barbell to bring me into balance. I also used the hot tub and some cold showers, but the quick five lifts seem to put me back into place.

Know the Role

That's the role of correctives. If you need surgery, go see a doctor. If you're so misaligned that every breath makes you nauseous, address that with more than some toe wiggling. Correctives have great value, but keep an eye on the prize.

Add some ground work, some half-kneeling effort and some big movements that will keep you in the game—but keep the intensity up so you can actually play the game when you get there.

A Novel Approach to Rest Periods

PEOPLE ASK ME TO SHARE training insights on everything from winter sports to the fighting arts. I help as I can, but quite often their questions are variations of, "Dan, I'm doing the One Lift a Day Program. If I add a second lift, will it still be one lift a day?"

The questions I can never get around to answering well deal with rest. How many seconds do you rest after a max deadlift? In my experience, three weeks. How long do you rest after a set of twenty-rep squats with 405 on your back? It seems to be somewhere between ten minutes and the next harvest moon.

Of all the topics in training, rest is the hardest for me to help others get a handle on.

Oh, I understand it. I've been there. I hadn't missed a workout in five years. I trained on Christmas day, heavy and hard. I worried over finding a gym on family vacations so I wouldn't miss a single front squat or heavy clean. I swallowed gag-inducing soy protein shakes that probably did more hormonal damage than good, and, when mixed with whole milk, turned slight acne into a burn-unit case. I did "everything right." No alcohol or marijuana touched these lips, and, sadly, few female lips, too.

And then, I melted down.

It was such an epic meltdown that when my wife met her current boss, he mentioned being from Montana. My wife laughed and said, "The only thing I know about Montana is that my husband got hit in the head by a discus there."

Tiff's new boss stiffened, "Oh my God, that was your husband?!"

Flashing back, I was standing outside the sector between throws talking to our assistant coach, Ferron Sonderegger (you just can't make up names like that), and his eyes widened. Before he could speak, I'd been hit in the skull by a two-kilo metal and wood discus that had just travelled about 140 feet through the air.

The impact should've killed me, but, well, the universe had other plans. The resulting personality change from the concussion did some interesting things. First, I made every bad decision I could for about five months, and I apologize for that.

Second, I totally lost some memories, as I had the chance to display at my Russian history class that next week. I sat down, looked up at Professor Glatfelter and said, "I don't remember anything."

But, the third was unexpected: I quit.

I stopped training. I stopped throwing. I quit school.

Somewhere around October, about five months after the hit to the head, I woke up. My handwriting returned, too. Well, it improved from illegible scrawl to awful.

And with that, I began rebuilding my life. I went back to school, started training again, and, to my surprise, was stronger than I'd ever been in my life. I threw the discus and hammer far farther than before, with less effort.

I'm still working on the insights I've unpacked from that experience. Part of the reason I'm so vague on rest, especially rest periods between sets, is that I see rest as a continuum that needs to be discussed in detail before moving on.

Eternal Rest

Let's start with the big one: eternal rest. This isn't a theology discussion, but as I always tell my athletes, "You can rest all you want when you're dead."

There are two sides of this first point: longevity and eternal life.

Longevity: Sadly, few gurus in the strength and conditioning field talk about longevity any more. We seem to only talk about health when it goes downhill.

"Living well as long as one can for as long as one can live well" is more than just my first attempt at a country western song. It's a reality for me.

As I walk closer each day to my death, the quality of life becomes more important. My doctor told me years ago that there are only two statistically relevant issues for living longer:

1. Don't smoke.

2. Wear your seatbelt.

Everything else is arguable. There are people living over a hundred who'll recommend a good cigar, as well as others who'll give frightening advice like "never drink booze."

But I'm not just interested in the number of my years; I worry about the quality of my time here on Earth.

Clearly, a sign of great aging is a relative abundance of lean body mass. I want to cling to muscle and keep bodyfat at bay for as long as I can. Hypertrophy training becomes even more important as we age.

In addition, the impact of a fifty-year athletic career has led me to believe that joint mobility trumps practically everything else when it comes to dealing with the ills of age. In other words, stay lean, muscular and loose for as long as you can.

As I continue to watch the sad lines of my friends die way too young, many times from the effects of youthful experimentation with drugs (often the performance-enhancing kind), I realize longevity is only important when it's your turn.

Eternal life: I'm not going to get into what happens after you die, but I've always believed the idea of "do to others what you'd want done to you" is a big factor in how things are going to end up on the "other side."

I've also embraced a teaching from Steve Ilg in his book *Total Body Transformation*. He asks a simple question: "When was the last time you picked up some litter?"

The other day, I cleaned up a neighborhood eyesore that's bugged me for weeks and felt lighter and happier. Each time I drive past it, I feel better.

Also, take some advice from one of my favorite characters in literature, the Alewife:

> *Gilgamesh, whither rovest thou?*
>
> *The life thou pursuest thou shall not find.*
>
> *When the gods created mankind,*
>
> *Death for mankind they set aside,*
>
> *Life in their own hands retaining.*
>
> *Thou, Gilgamesh, let full be thy belly.*
>
> *Make thou merry by day and by night.*
>
> *Of each day make thou a feast of rejoicing,*
>
> *Day and night dance thou and play.*
>
> *Let thy garments be sparkling fresh,*
>
> *Thy head be washed; bathe thou in water.*
>
> *Pay heed to the little one that holds on to thy hand,*

Let thy spouse rejoice in thy bosom!

For this is the task of mankind!

The Role of Rest

The Alewife leads us to the next point, where's the role of rest in your life? For years, I've been giving a workshop that discusses a point I was taught in the second grade. Now, if something I learned in the early 1960s still impacts my thinking and teaching today, it's worthy of discussion.

My teacher went to the board and put up four words where North, South, East, and West would be on a compass. They were "play," "pray," "rest" and "work."

Then she made her point: In life, these four things must be balanced. If one gets too far apart, like work, you'll slowly burn out. If you play all the time, like the grasshopper in the story *The Grasshopper and the Ant,* you'll have to catch up when things go wrong (and they always go wrong). Praying could simply be alone time or your efforts to do those internal exercises that keep us going along.

Rest is the problem for many of us today, as we tend to stay up later and later, cutting into our sleep time. Also, working sixty hours a week leaves little time to take care of rest!

I listen closely to people who build an understanding of this concept into their programs. Ilg's *Total Body Transformation* is a handbook of bringing strength training, yoga, meditation, nutrition and life together into one system. I've always enjoyed blending the two-headed monster of brutal, grinding strength training with insightful, even artistic, flexibility and mobility work.

That compass of rest, play, pray and work illuminates my life. Certainly, I've ignored it throughout my years (just read my other books for examples of my idiocy), but when I'm at my best, I attempt to tie together these four points in all my life.

A Few Examples
Wine Walks

Long walks are an underappreciated element in strength training. I'm not talking about packing on plates and sleds and attacking a mountain; I'm thinking of what my wife and I do on occasion. I have this specialty backpack that holds a bottle of wine, glasses and an opener. We go for a long, easy walk and find a suitable place to pop the cork, talk about life, laugh and enjoy nature and our relationship. (The walk back is always interesting.)

Meat Fests

We have a tradition of bringing a bunch of people over to our house to train. Because of the numbers, we have to move to the way back where we set up the Highland game equipment, weights, sleds, kettlebells and odd stuff. The group dynamic tends to lead to long, fun workouts with some challenges and a lot of laughs. We all bring cuts of meat and end with a long party of meat and drinks.

Throw Training

One of the ways I prepare myself for competition is to bring a kettlebell out to a field with my discus (or whatever implement is going to be part of the next competition). I combine throwing with various kettlebell drills for as long as I need to be there. I try to just keep finding the small spaces in my body to stretch out with the kettlebell and try to carry this feeling over into my throwing. I try to go "inside" during this time and block out everything and everyone else. Oddly, most of my writing ideas seem to pop into my head during these workouts, especially those where I decide I need to talk about rest.

I could argue that mixing these three workouts would be an ideal way to train. It certainly has the feel for covering all the keys to training. Notice how the four elements of play, pray, work and rest naturally come together in these workouts. Take a few minutes to assess your life and see if any of these elements are missing.

And if you work, work, work…keep your eyes open for a discus.

Layoffs and Vacations

The next stop on my continuum of rest is to understand layoffs and vacations. I seem to constantly give conflicting information. For example, if you want to lose fat, stop talking and give me twenty-eight days of the Velocity Diet. If you want flexibility, sign up for a thirty-day yoga challenge and give it a go.

I also give this advice: Take six weeks off.

What? It's something I've never done on purpose. Oh, sure, after this surgery or that surgery, I took time off, and when I got really sick, I took two whole weeks off.

In hindsight, I should've listened to a friend who studied sports training in another country. I asked him about American athletic training. His response, "Well, the consensus is that you're all overtrained."

"What about me?"

"Dan, you're the poster child for overtraining."

Off the top of my head, I'd suggest that a hard-training athlete take about six weeks off a year. And I mean off. No basketball tournaments, no spin bike classes, nothing.

Now, the sad thing is this: basically, those of you who don't train hard just decided to take the next six weeks off. Those who train hard will take those six weeks off when they're dead.

I never understood taking time off until far too late in my career. I remember Dan Cantore, fresh from the 1976 Olympics, telling me he was taking some time to "regroup."

My thought was, "The next Olympics are just four years away!" I could have had "more career" with more "regrouping."

In the same vein, when you go on vacation, go on vacation. Don't try to keep your normal training going. Now, having said this, I also find that visiting a weightroom or gym on a trip allows me to meet a bunch of new people and enjoy experiences that might not happen otherwise. You need to make a choice as to whether you want to have a fun minimal workout on vacations, but I also enjoy the free food and drinks that always seem to follow my little coaching pointers in an alien gym.

There's also a lot to be said for active rest.

It's a term that's been around for decades but is still overlooked. It's this idea: For a few weeks, instead of doing your basic training, get involved in some other activity.

Famously, the Soviet athletes got into volleyball, so much so that several weightlifters achieved Masters of Sport in the game. The German discus throwers used to enjoy downhill skiing, and it's hard to imagine American athletes who don't enjoy pickup basketball games.

Enjoy active rest long enough to realize that your gifts are probably not good enough for the NBA.

The Wonders of Sleep

Sleep, the daily cure for all that ails you, is still overlooked as the key to recovery. Years ago, after reading *Lights Out: Sleep, Sugar, and Survival,* by T. S. Wiley, I came away with the courage to do a famous experiment on myself. I'd try to sleep up to twelve hours a day for a week. The bodyfat dripped off of me that week, and I had to force myself to eat.

For the heck of it, I decided to follow that path again. As I am typing this, I'm coming off a twelve-hour snooze. Yesterday, I only got nine hours of sleep, but was able to sneak in a three-hour nap in the afternoon. Napping is underrated and worthy of your attention.

The first time I tried this experiment, I went from 226 to 214 in about six days. I ate zero carbs, save one salad, and really feasted on eggs and coffee. I'm still bravely working on this protocol, but I did sneak on the scale yesterday and saw I was 222. That's less than I weighed when I finished the Velocity Diet.

On the V-Diet, I ate nothing but enjoyed six shakes a day. On this diet, I lie around in bed. You decide which one is easier.

Not long ago, I was called out on another forum for "pimping" supplements. Bah, I say to you. I do things that work. If they work, I tell you about them. One may note I don't tell you everything I try because not everything you pop in your mouth works like promised. (Where's my bee pollen?)

There are some supplements I use every night to help with sleep.

Years ago, I had two friends divorce their wives and make very poor decisions over the course of about two years. One buddy ended up in federal prison as a result of his decisions. Talking with both of them, they had one common sentence, "I can't sleep through the night. I only get about four hours." After a few months of no sleep, they both started making bizarre choices.

I learned from that lesson: Lack of sleep is not only hard on your training; it's hard on your life.

First, invest in a good bed, good pillows and adequate blinds. We buy new pillows at least once a year, usually twice. We take the old pillows on trips or use them in the television room. You spend a third of your life in bed, so invest wisely.

Second, about a half an hour before I go to bed, I take the following:

- ZMA
- Fish oil
- A serving of sugar-free Metamucil

With a glass of wine, you can feel the body relax. I think magnesium continues to be the most underrated of supplements, and its wonderful calming effects combined with its wonders for the bowels keeps it as my first-place winner as supplement of the year.

If you have a hard time sleeping, read before bed, but don't watch television or play on the internet. If you need books that'll put you to sleep, try the *Twilight* series. (Oh, meow!)

For napping, you can only do what you can do. I have a small cot at work, and I found a place no one will bother me for about twenty minutes, and I'm not telling you where that is!

Some suggest eye shades and those airline neck pillows, and that might be a good idea. If you can nap, do it. The tradition among elite track and Olympic lifting athletes is a daily nap. I asked a Russian friend for the technical term for this afternoon nap and he gave me an odd Russian term: siesta.

The Least Important Rest

Now let's look at what I consider the least important concept in rest: the rest period between sets.

I'm always amazed when I read massive twelve-week training programs and the author has given us varied rest periods for every lift and movement for every workout of every day of the program.

My experience is that rarely do people follow a workout plan for two days, much less eighty-four.

But there those numbers sit patiently.

In the past, rest periods were given in minutes, but today there's a move to seconds. When I'm training hard, my awful math skills degenerate so much that I have no idea how long 240 seconds is, so I just wait about four minutes and go.

Here's the issue, and most strong and accomplished people would agree: For an accomplished trainer, rest periods are more fluid. When Vasily Alekseyev clean and jerked 500 pounds for the first time in Columbus in 1970, how long did he rest before he added weight to do another? It's a crazy statement to even make. A novice trainer doing a set of ten benches on a machine can repeat that performance very quickly.

The genius of measuring rest periods is that you can honestly compare one workout to another. I've found that sets, reps and load only tell part of the story in a standard workout. In my favorite workout scheme—three sets of eight with one minute of rest between sets—I can gauge how I'm doing literally from year to year, and, in the case of overhead squats and front squats, from decade to decade.

Without the truth of the rest period, you're comparing apples to oranges, or whatever cliché fits the day.

In some workouts, the rest-to-work ratio is the workout. Kenneth Jay's Viking Warrior training of mixing fifteen seconds of kettlebell snatches with fifteen seconds of active rest for up to forty minutes is an attempt to drive your VO2 max through the roof. The oft-misunderstood Tabata protocol is supposed to feel awful and difficult from the first set. It is not twenty seconds of hand waving, ten seconds of rest and twenty seconds of something else.

As described in my article *Fat Loss in Four Minutes,* most people think the workout is a fun change of pace. The actual twenty seconds on and ten seconds off with front squats is a way to ruin several days in a row.

Putting It to Rest

When I get asked about rest, I get lost in this continuum. From literally death to the details of a small part of a workout, rest means a lot. It shouldn't be considered something to do when you're done, but we should actively think about resting.

To Summarize

1. I'm not against giving advice about rest periods between sets; it's just that I think there are many other keys to discuss before I say you need 118 seconds between sets of reverse sumo curls in the Smith machine.
2. Since most of the information concerning rest is free (no one charges you for sleep), there's no market, and therefore you don't hear much about it.
3. Truly, any balance you bring to your training will help. Taking the time and effort to intelligently add rest will pay off better than buying a new curl machine.

Don't take a discus to the head to learn the importance of rest and recovery.

On Drinking and Phenomenology

In 2004 I wrote a book for my daughter Kelly when she graduated from the eighth grade. Since my folks had died relatively young, I wanted to make sure those odd tidbits of wisdom that had floated across my life would be stored somewhere. So, I gave her *From Dad to Grad.* You can find it on my site for free or get it on Kindle (and give it a five-star review because there are only two kinds of Amazon reviews...five-star and "this book sukcs and the writer needs tobe a ggooder writer").

For those of you who are worried: Lindsay received *A Father's Legacy* two years later upon her graduation. It's a handwritten book that I wrote by answering literally page after page after page of very good questions.

But, for Kelly's book I followed the traditional essay style of writing that best translates into English as "attempts." Following Montaigne, I entitled each chapter "On..." and covered a topic with some attempts at wisdom and wit. Even today, the parts on suitable dressing and being thankful are good advice for everyone and every situation.

Of course, as she was in the eighth grade, not all topics were appropriate. Lately I've been working on another book, and I spend a lot of time on epistemology—basically, how you know what you know.

Personally, eighty percent of what I know comes from either experts in the field I'm working in (the authority method) or a distillation of what the best in the field are doing (a form of deductive logic).

Yet we must always keep an eye out for new research, new tools and new ways of doing things. I figure that's good for about ten percent of how I do things.

In other words, if you are a discus thrower, you're going to hear me imitate Ralph Maughan in technique and Dick Notmeyer in the weightroom.

The best throwers are lifting with basic movements. Now, when the biomech guys studied the discus, most of their insights were answered with "Um…yeah." But, the concept of the way the axis turns in the middle of the throw made me totally buy into both the simple ("Turn your right foot") and the more complex ("I need to explain 3B to you"). Don't worry about the terms, just understand that science and research can really help, but, frankly, it's only the icing on the cake of experience.

I also believe we can all add a magnificent contribution to each and every field. You have the insights and experiences to illuminate something that will make the next generation of authorities have even greater clarity.

I wrote this in *Fat Loss Happens on Monday:*

> *What we need to do is seek out what the BEST are doing and follow that path. Unless you invent a brand new sport or game or activity, someone else has been on this road before you. Follow the recipe before you try to play with some new spices.*

Phenomenology is a term we used quite a bit during my studies in religious education. I never understood the term well enough at first as we were being smothered by the volume of reading and discussion each week. One professor summarized the method of answering a question in the Jesuit tradition of education:

Never Deny.

Rarely Affirm.

Always Distinguish.

So, when you were confused by something, it didn't always help to raise your hand and ask the professor. So, I asked my classmate. She explained it to me like this:

"Imagine a well in the middle of a village. Someone walks up to it and tells you that there is water at the bottom. I walk up to it and notice a couple of stones. Then, you come over and point out the frog on the stone. That's what we are talking about here."

Phenomenology gives us the great insight about how the authority and deductive logic models interact, inform and improve one's insights, experience and emotions concerning training. It also gives you understanding that if one of our students sees the frog, we are all better for it and we can share that with the body of knowledge.

Good coaches and trainers know this in their hearts and minds. I ask my athletes to "one day" write me a note about what they learned during their time with me. I actually prefer they write it when they are working and have families. What do they say? Well, I call them "gems" for a reason.

One athlete, an undervalued high school discus thrower but three-time conference champ in college, John Richardson, noted that I have this phrase I used all the time: "They can't all be gems." It relates to good throws versus bad throws, but he found this a great way to walk through life, work, and relationships. Not all days will be perfect. They can't all be gems. But some will.

Later, I added this little line to further explain this point: "This isn't moral theology. There is no good or bad here. That was simply a throw (or a lift or a jump or whatever). Stop judging it and get back to practice." John saw the frog and now I can point it out to every athlete who comes along after him.

So…this was supposed to be about drinking?

Well, it is. First, let me frame it a bit. It will sound like a rant.

I'm sick of dealing with snotty twenty-year-old girls in black dresses at restaurants.

I should point out that the root of "restaurants" is the same as "restoratives" and all the rest of those great recovery tools, but I digress.

This whole show about waiting for the tables and all the rest has to move along. Part two of this experience is when I order wine.

Listen: I know wine. I have autographed bottles from some of the biggest names in the field (some bottles still full!), and I have strong opinions on wine. First, this little rule about white wine and white meats (poultry, fish and, I guess, pork) is, at best, a suggestion.

Pinot noir goes well with salmon in my world. White wines? Chardonnay has gone from being wonderful two decades ago to tasting like butter on a wooden table. I see little difference between the two. As for "goes with turkey," Sauvignon blanc has slowly become more like licking granite.

But, I digress again! Certainly, there are red wines that hold up to the rule "Red wines with red meat," but some are made for simply enjoying whatever you are simply enjoying (Malbec and Pinot noir).

When it comes to hard liquor, I've come to some interesting conclusions. I'm a fan of Scotch whiskey (Scots whisky is also correct), and am sick of people telling me about the glories of single malts. I get it, you like peat. You like ashtrays.

Mostly, I am just joking around here, but I want to explain an interesting thing we have done for the past few years and that has become a popular Christmas tradition. We do a blind taste test.

It changed the way I drink alcohol and how I pair things with food. Everyone is given a chance to sit in judgment as the rest of us heckle them. We blindfold you and give you the chance to sip five different beverages. If you are a bourbon drinker, five bourbons. For the record, no one gets inebriated during these events as there's only a sip or two in each glass. And only one person goes at a time.

With Johnnie Walker, we put out Red, Black, Green, Gold and Blue, although today we have Platinum and the new Spice. Red has that band-aid odor that's easily discerned and Green is peaty. Oddly, the lower price Black tends to defeat Gold and Blue (well over $200 a bottle). In bourbon tasting, Jack Daniels tends to win in the blind test over far more expensive choices, and that makes shopping in the future much cheaper.

Wait, what am I talking about?

Certainly, I'm talking about drinking, but I want you to "hear" what's underneath this whole conversation: your experiences—your senses—should be a major factor in your decision-making process. If you're a fast-food eater, are you letting various clowns, Chihuahuas and mice dictate your taste buds? Test it out! Blind taste a bite of various burgers, tacos or pizza and let yourself become the decider.

I'm trying to give you permission to use phenomenology in your life. In the past months at our gym, we've had people doing a variety of programs from other gyms, trainers and books to test the deep waters of the well. And, by the way, to the LETTER, no tweaking to improve it!

If you decide to dive in on a diet or exercise program, go all in. Test it. Finish it. Then, check your notes and critique it.

Oh, that whole "finish it" thing. Yeah. Good idea. I had an idiot critique my book *Never Let Go* (the one similar to this one), and he wrote something like "Overhead squats and front squats. That's about it." By God, at least turn the pages a little!

If you tell me you're on a twelve-week strength program, don't email me at six weeks to ask about a three-week program. I'm no math whiz, but I know this is wrong.

The point of this whole chapter is this: trust those who have gone before us in any field of endeavor, but don't be afraid to add your own insights and experiences. I'm giving you permission to do this!

And, more important, you might unpack, open up, illuminate and clarify something the rest of us might wish we'd have known a long time ago.

Follow it. Finish it. Share what you found.

Figuring Out Your Life and Lifting Goals

As you already know, I'm a huge fan of Steve Ilg's book *Total Body Transformation*. In the introduction, he makes a small point that continues to shape my understanding of training, health and life.

Very simply, he notes that the word "fit" comes from the Old Norse meaning "to knit." I can't think of a better way to describe, in the most basic terms, the goals of life.

If you're familiar with my work, you've probably noticed my most common response to a question begins with, "What's your goal?"

For instance, if someone is Olympic lifting and wants to try to increase load without burning out, I often recommend the One Lift a Day program.

Now, a fourteen-year-old boy from Iowa who wants to be Mr. Olympia, play in the NBA and become a Navy SEAL might not benefit from this program. Goal setting is a crucial part of any discussion concerning training.

Some ideas just don't work, even though they're fun to read about or watch our friends do. I see all manner of strange, bizarre and quirky moves at workshops, conventions and on blogs. People are using balls, slides, ropes and stretchy bands to do every imaginable lateral lunge—and I still think a heavy back squat trumps the whole lot of them.

If standing on a BOSU ball juggling kettlebells with a stretchy band around your knees is driving you to your particular goal, well, bless you and carry on.

But most would be better served considering Ilg's insight: Fitness is knitting.

An old friend of mine who died not long ago once told me that "life is a tapestry." These threads from here and there knit together to form you as a person, and Ilg's work is a great example of this. Yoga, strength training, cardio, nutrition and meditation are his pillars, but you also find his insights about life, living and everything (with apologies to Douglas Adams).

With that in mind, I'd like to suggest a few ideas about seeing training and fitness goals as part of a larger tapestry of life.

Get on the Success Track

First, there's an old saying: "Success leaves tracks."

Growing up, I was lucky that *Strength and Health* magazine came out once a month. I'd read about the training of football players and track athletes and realized I had to get stronger. Gary Ordway, an elite American discus thrower, had these numbers in his pre-season training:

> *Squats: 505 × 3*
> *Deadlift: 455 × 3*
> *Power clean: 285 × 2*
> *Incline press: 325 × 3*
> *Situps: 4 sets of 25*

When I read that article, I saw the road from my lifts to his lifts wouldn't be overnight. But at least I knew the path! My eighty-five-pound incline barbell press—and pardon me for bragging, but I was doing eight reps with it—was a bit shy of his load.

In my travels, I enjoy visiting college campuses and researching old articles and materials. Recently, I found an old *American Athlete* article that discussed how America's best shot put and discus thrower at the time, L. Jay Silvester, added deadlifts to his training.

The article discussed how a 400-pound deadlift would help him improve his marks "even more." That's a lift routinely done by high school sophomore football players now.

That most fundamental lesson of my career was clear by age fourteen: lifting weights and getting stronger would support my goals.

The lesson I missed was that "enough is enough" when it comes to strength.

L. Jay, for example, threw 210 feet with his 400-pound deadlift. At the same time in my career, I threw 190 with a 628-pound deadlift.

The toughest issue for me to wrap my mind around is still that we need just to be strong enough. Certainly, I guess we could add flexible enough, mobile enough and enough of enough is enough, but we need to get to certain standards and then do our best to stay there.

How do you find out those standards? Ask those who've been on this road before you.

A certain Austrian boy named Arnold competed in Olympic lifting meets and snatched 242 and clean and jerked 303. Other great bodybuilders, including Sergio Oliva and Franco Columbu, competed on the platform. No, Arnold's numbers aren't earth-shattering, but they're pretty good—good enough to support one of the best bodies in history.

How strong should you be? Here are some standards I've used with success:

Men

Push

Expected: Bodyweight bench press
Game changer: Bodyweight bench press for 15 reps

Pull

Expected: 8–10 pullups
Game changer: 15 pullups

Squat

Expected: Bodyweight squat
Game changer: Bodyweight squat for 15 reps

Hinge

Expected: Bodyweight to 150% bodyweight deadlift
Game changer: Double-bodyweight deadlift

Loaded Carry (Farmer Walk)

Expected: Farmer walk with total bodyweight (half per hand)
Game changer: Bodyweight per hand

I used to use different terms than "expected" and "game changer," but no matter. I recommend the basic training templates if you haven't reached the minimum level expected. You honestly don't need much more than linear periodization and perhaps a few minutes or hours on the basics of technique.

If you have game-changing numbers across all five movements, well, let's just say the weightroom isn't your problem unless you're in a pure strength sport like powerlifting or Olympic lifting or strongman competition.

The distance of the farmer walk will vary, but let's assume something as short as forty meters.

For women, any strength training seems to help. Even though I've been chasing appropriate standards, the chasm between the drugged and the clean has made it hard to find solid numbers. Honestly, I used to think any lifting was a pretty good beginning.

These are the current numbers I'm using with women:

Women

Push

Game changer: Bodyweight bench press

Pull

Game changer: 3 pullups

Squat

Game changer: 135-pound back squat for 5 reps

Hinge

Game changer: 275-pound deadlift

Loaded Carry (Farmer Walk)

Game changer: 85 pounds per hand

Once a woman reaches all five levels in all five movements, good things tend to happen in the field of play. I know these numbers might be considered low, but it's the balance across the five that seems most important for athletes.

Moreover, achieving all five levels tends to support this notion of knitting. If you have the appropriate levels of strength for your goals, look beyond the weightroom for the reasons you're not achieving them.

If your goal is fat loss, look at the plates on the table, not the plates in the gym.

A Case for Failure?

Second, failure also leaves tracks.

I lost my training journal and hated losing it, as this is, or was, my gold mine. I could trace injuries, illness and competitive failures back through the days, weeks and months leading up to the moment things came unglued.

As I look back over a career that takes us back to the Johnson administration, I can pull out failure after failure. Sometimes not achieving a goal or a dream spurs people into making a greater impact on the world than fulfilling it. And the reverse is true, too: getting that dream can flatten a person for years to come.

I've known a lot of college English majors who spent four years writing in creative writing and poetry classes and then never write another essay as long as they live. They may spend hours red-penning in semicolons and the words "transitive verb" above a student's paper, but never again write a composition. They attained the degree—and stopped writing.

Many athletes sweat and fight for four years of high school to get a scholarship to college, then quit after the first weeks of college practice because "it doesn't mean anything" to them.

Mark Twight, the author of *Kiss or Kill* and one of the world's foremost mountain climbers, noted the same thing at our dinner table not long ago. Faced with a decision to keep climbing and probably die on Mount Everest or to come back to base camp, he came back down. But, he noted, he learned far more from this failure than he would have from succeeding.

In a sense, success can dilute the lessons of life.

No, I'm not telling you to fail; it's just that failure seems to prod most people into rethinking the attempts, the journey and the path.

Joseph Campbell commented several times that the most renowned person in comparative religion never got his doctorate. Campbell chose not to do it, and often encouraged his students to not go on either.

He also warned them of getting buttonholed in a job that stopped them from exploring all the directions life presented them. He noted people who earned their terminal degrees and were appointed to their dream jobs often "flattened" out.

Much like Earl Nightingale warned us, "A rut is a grave with the ends kicked out."

Every four years, the world turns its attention on the Olympic sports for a few weeks. I'm not exaggerating when I tell you that one of the worst kept secrets of Olympic sports is how many of the athletes quit the sport after the Olympics.

Even gold medalists abandon the pool, track, field and court. After all the sacrifice and pain, "Here's your medal, thank you very much, next!" just doesn't fulfill the athletes as much as the dreams of victory during training.

Those who fail to make their goals turn to coaching, writing or other forms to continue expressing themselves in other media. Or they take those lessons learned and parlay them into a successful life, but they don't just drop them and walk away.

143

Now, I'm not encouraging failure or the initiating of a "culture of failure." But I coached football at Judge Memorial Catholic High School for a long time and I realized a very unsettling thing: when we began losing games, the athletes were getting more out of losing than the winners did from winning.

When you win a game, as I had the good fortune to do when playing for South San Francisco High School, the team goes into the locker room and before you untie your shoes, the coach is talking about next week. The total amount of celebration in a winning locker room—for true winners—is...not very much.

As for the losers? The losers have hugs, tears, long heart-tugging speeches and kisses from the prettiest girls. While the victors are thinking of yet another week on the grindstone, the losers are being cuddled and caressed back to a smile.

Don't let success flatten you nor let failure push you into the Loser's Club. Learn from failure, enjoy it if you can, but plug along into another expedition to the top.

When you win, be gracious.

When you get your goals, dream up other goals.

Find a Worthy Mentor

Is there an easier way to learn how to achieve your goals and learn from failure?

Actually there is, and it's my third insight: Pick good lifelong mentors.

This is not what most people think. I'm not talking about those who guide, coach or teach you. What I'm saying is that you should carefully watch someone who is ten, twenty or thirty years older than you, someone you admire and salute the success in life, learning and lifting.

In my case, my positive role model has always been Dick Notmeyer. When my family first met him, he was forty-seven and looked to be in his early thirties. He trained with very basic movements, took his supplements and drank protein drinks every day. He looked and moved great.

When the great jogging boom hit, Dick got swept up in it along with his friends, and lost some of his shoulder mass and looked older. When Dick dropped the jogging and began cycling and lifting, he looked younger again!

Dick not only taught me how to Olympic lift, he also taught me the value of combining lifting and cardio throughout a lifetime. The key, it seems, is not to let the cardio side destroy the muscle mass.

As I've since noted that after age twenty-eight, the body seems to conspire to lose lean body mass and stiffen up. Jogging, while certainly better than nothing, tends to waste some muscle mass and lock up the joints. Runners turn to everything to deal with injuries, from arch support, weird shoes, yoga and herbal concoctions. The alternative, as I learned from watching Dick, is to just lift and get some crashless cardio in.

Certainly there were others I learned from. One thing that's clear is that alpha males tend to hang around the sports I compete in. The day of the competition is the day to shine.

Alas, that's not what most guys in the throws and lifting sports understand. If a stupid challenge somehow presents itself, it becomes:

"Watch this!"

"Hold my beer!"

"Get your video camera ready!"

As anyone with an internet connection knows, this is where things tend to go badly. Among those of us us who came up as throwers in the 1970s, the bulk of the injuries are from doing something extremely stupid. Blown biceps from challenges, hamstrings torn off the bone from doing something the human body wasn't designed to do, and dislocated shoulders from trying to prove the shoulder joint can really do much more than God thought it should do.

When I also think about the number of friends I've lost to heart attacks and bad choices, I'm happy I avoided those life-altering bad choices.

I remember the dozen or so friends who are dead or crippled from bad choices, and I'm happy I was lucky enough to have "chosen wisely," as the knight in *Indiana Jones and the Last Crusade* reminded us.

Think about the life you want to live ten, twenty or thirty years from now, and observe someone who is living that way now. I wanted to be healthy, wealthy and wise, so I observed, followed and studied those who had that and tried to do what they did.

Your goals and dreams should be intertwined with threads of career, family and community, as well as fitness, health and body composition. Certainly that seventeen-inch arm is a noteworthy goal, but be sure to knit it with a lifetime vision of health and success.

Study those who have achieved your goals and follow their tracks. Learn from failures along the way and even embrace them, as the price of failure is so high.

Finally, take some time to "go back to the future" by looking at those who are a few decades older than you and reflect the lifestyle you want to eventually have.

Knit all of this together for a fit life.

Going from Point A to Point B

PEOPLE OFTEN ASK ME HOW LONG I've been teaching and coaching. I like to say, long enough that I have stories that start with kids who are teenagers and end with them contacting me as they approach their fiftieth birthday.

I was handing back a test one day when I heard two high school dancers whisper about what a bitch Miss X was, along with some comments about her "fat ass."

Unbeknownst to the two girls—or anyone—I was dating Miss X at the time and, well, you can trust me that the issue was overstated. (That said, further comments by me on this particular supposedly large body part will be reserved for the good of my marriage to Tiffini, who was not the lovely Miss X.)

Ten years later, I'm locking the door to the school and I hear a squeal, "Mr. John." I didn't recognize the two figures running at me as the sun had been momentarily eclipsed by the effects of years of feeding off beer and pizza. Let's just say if there's such thing as a "Dharma Boomerang," the universe had hit those two girls right in the posterior.

Anyway, I've been around so long that my former students use some of my old assignments to teach their classes today.

One such assignment that's worthy of anyone's time is called, "My Life Is My Message."

It was intended as a way to ask questions of the students that made them think about who they are today and how that should impact their future.

It starts off simple, like "What are your ten favorite movies?"

My list is updated every few years, but here's the exact list from a couple of decades ago:

- *Patton*
- *Star Trek II: The Wrath of Khan*
- *Lawrence of Arabia*
- *Star Wars* (The real first one, I think they call it IV now)
- *Field of Dreams*
- *Animal House*
- *The Three Musketeers* (with Michael York)
- *Robin Hood* (Errol Flynn)
- *Brigadoon*
- *How to Succeed in Business Without Really Trying*

I also ask for top ten books (if you're a book lover looking for a future spouse and your betrothed has never finished ten books, well, there's a red flag for you), top five albums (Miles Davis' *Porgy and Bess* and Frank Sinatra's *A Man Alone* make my list), and, from the insights of Sean Greeley, I now ask for Ten Favorite Meals (not foods—the gatherings).

The assignment culminated in a ten-year plan, and students instantly realized the burden of debt, the importance of getting degrees, traveling as quickly as possible and taking care of fitness and physique.

Sadly, not everyone follows the logical and right path. I've had more than one student tell me, "I was smarter at seventeen than twenty-seven."

This is a form of goal setting, and it's like mining a vein of pure gold for the chances of success in life.

I made my mark in this field helping people look at big picture goals, and I'm proud that many people think I'm a "go to" guy for goal setting.

But, as good as the toolkit I offer, I've recently discovered that I'm also an idiot.

I had great ideas, excellent programming and some nice technical tidbits that worked for everyone. For the squat, I had progressions that I humbly believe changed the world of lifting forever.

Well, at least, I thought they were working. I recently discovered I was saying "this," but people were hearing "that." I thought I was making a point, but people were disconnecting and hearing something else.

The Math Class Solution

This program is all about getting people to their goals. As the cliché goes, "If you don't know where you're going, any road will get you there!"

I also need to add the old Irish joke: "I need to get to Dublin. Can you show me the way?"

"Well, I wouldn't start from here!"

This was the disconnect. I was expecting people to know where they were going and, at least with the serious trainees, exactly where they wanted to go (Olympics, Super Bowl, ten percent bodyfat, whatever).

Since many knew exactly where they wanted to go, I got full of myself and convinced myself this was the norm. But many, as I soon learned, had no concept of where they were heading, and my advice was just another road.

I'm reminded of math class, by far my weakest subject:

"The shortest distance between two points is a straight line."

With the group who knew exactly where they were headed, success is like a math problem. The fastest way from Point A—where you are—to Point B—where you want to go—is a straight line. My athletes always seemed to know they wanted to go to Point B!

The issue is, sure, they knew about Point B. But Point A, where they are right now, was sometimes a deep mystery.

Welcome to my approach to coaching those with clear goals: Identify where they are now.

Some laugh at this.

"Um, isn't that obvious?"

Really? Consider this: I've had people realize their short-term goal needed so many new skills that they simply didn't have enough time in the day to learn them all.

These people were asking for my advice, and having no idea what they wanted to get from the conversation.

And the result was, I couldn't really help them.

I'm sorry, but if you're going to listen to every voice in the wind, I don't think I can be one of them. One can easily find a new diet and weight loss idea every day of the week in magazines and on the internet.

I often note, "I didn't get enough food on this new diet, so now I'm on two diets."

Well, if you don't know your goal, following two diets at once is probably just as good as anything else I can encourage you to try.

This approach, my friends, is all about discovering where you are. Now, since this is also the first question that God asks Adam in Genesis, I have to be a little careful about treading on copyright violations.

With elite athletes and trainees, we spend the bulk of our time discovering "where they are." Do they have the tools necessary for the goal? Do they have the skills, like a solid squat? Do they have the corrective movements mapped out, and do they know what needs to be corrected?

Once we map out Point A, we discover a straight line. Now, it might seem to be longer than the time allotted for the original goal, but at least we can honestly begin walking down the path to success.

When I've worked with some wonderful ladies, they have the exact opposite issue, and the honesty brings them to tears:

"I am just so heavy…so fat."

"I can't control this thing…and," shaking an upper arm, "what is this?"

"My husband won't touch me."

It's hard to hear, to be honest. But, this clarity about where they are, Point A, is stunning. They know they need to exercise and eat better.

Welcome to the Disconnect. Most people know Point A (I'm fat, need to exercise, and need to eat better), but Point B is the issue. These fine ladies see the photoshopped images on fitness magazines and think that's Point B.

Recently, a young singer released a before-and-after photo where her legs got longer, her waist came in and her boobs got bigger—yet this all happened in the artist's studio.

Folks, Point B is the issue for most of us. We're living in this odd time where photos of hyper-fit women with both genetic gifts and serious augmentation for any missing blanks dominate the fitness industry. This, frankly, is Point Z for most, not Point B!

I applaud Josh Hillis and others who have been using realistic bodyfat pictures to help clients find their goals. As Josh tells me, nineteen percent bodyfat for a woman is rock star hot, but twenty-five percent looks fantastic, too.

Sadly, our industry uses Photoshop, vomiting and surgery to achieve the illusion of health and fitness. We need to take Josh's advice and show some reasonableness.

So, here's our triple-edged sword that must be addressed:

- For whatever reason, some people, often athletes, clearly see the goal.
- Some people know exactly where they are physically, but need help seeing a realistic goal.
- There are others, of course, who are far from reality on either Point A and Point B, and we need to work both ends with them.

Missing this point has muddled my whole career. This is why we need to do assessments like the FMS early and often, taking "before" pictures (so you can take the "after"), do basic strength tests and those I outlined in *Can You Go*.

This is why we need to have food journals and proactive calendars to note the things that are coming up and will impede progress or training, and when things will ease up so we can accelerate to the goals.

We need to know where you are.

When I first began to do Easy Strength, the forty-day program of repeating the same lifts each and every day for just a set or two, the program freed up a lot of time, energy and intensity so I could work on the other qualities that were demanded of me as a thrower.

I had the weightroom locked down, but needed more correctives (I'm Mr. Asymmetrical, Novice Class, Open Division) and some technical throwing issues to address.

When I work with almost everyone else, addressing poor squat technique and lack of loaded carries makes a near-immediate difference in their bodies and the ability to train. But for me, easy strength—or even easier strength—is how to best get to Point B.

But you need to assess! Some will need focused time in the weightroom retooling and re-schooling the issues; then, we can get back to the issues of technique, tactics and all the other tools.

With our friend who has no vision of where to go besides those celebrity diets that invade the checkout line, we need to point to a reasonable path to success. It might be food preparation, shopping skills, movement issues or whatever. It also includes realistic next steps and, even more importantly, realistic goals.

So, let's sum this up:

- If people know the goal, assess where they are now and connect the dots.
- If people know where they are now, but are either begging for a miracle or clueless about the next step, show them the next step and connect the dots.
- And finally, for everyone you coach or mentor, focus constantly on the process and on the keys to success.

It's a lesson I've learned over a long time in the field.

Five Reasons You Don't Look Like You Lift

THERE ARE PLENTY OF THINGS we can do wrong in our training, but if we could get people to fix some of them, the world would be a stronger, fitter place.

1. You're Forgetting to Actually Train

A timer goes off the moment you enter the gym. Think of it as one of those countdown clocks on an explosive device in an action movie. Each of us has a different total amount of time programmed in, but regardless, it starts when you walk in.

What you do in the first ten minutes of training will tell me just about everything I need to know about what you do right and what you do wrong. I used to tell people to front squat first. This is still good advice, but I was hoping a hint of urgency would ignite some people to think about the importance of getting into the gym and going to work.

With this new era of corrective work, I see people writhing on the walls with lacrosse balls against their spine, flailing on the floor with foam rollers and following a packaged program guaranteed to realign their Virgo across Scorpio. Then there's twenty minutes of easy treadmilling, some dynamic mobility and let's finish with some stable stability or whatever.

One hour after entering the gym they can proudly acknowledge they did practically nothing. And then it's time to go.

In addition to the countdown clock, think of the gym time as a sandbag. As we enter, we cut a small hole in our ability to train, and the sand starts pouring out. When empty, we have nothing left. In other words, if we waste all that sand doing silly stuff, there's none left for the stuff that actually makes us stronger, fitter or a better athlete.

This isn't saying some of those tools aren't useful, but do you need all of them, at once, before every workout?

Many of us are tricking ourselves into thinking we're training when really we're just wandering in off the street and wasting time. Stop it.

2. You Have Workout ADD

The fix for problem Number One is to follow a program. I have one rule regarding programs: I don't care what program you're doing, just finish it. Start it and finish it.

I have a mass-building program in the book called *Mass Made Simple*—fourteen workouts over six weeks. I ask you to give up two to three hours of your time each week to lift, press and squat until you can squat bodyweight for fifty reps. Start it, finish it.

Maybe mass isn't your issue right now, but what is? And don't say "fat loss" either, as the bulk of people training (ha, bulk!) will give that answer.

The trouble is, even though they're presumably focusing on fat loss, they rarely make any progress.

Why not focus on something else and see if fat drops along with improving some other quality? Most programs are about six weeks long, so if it's a disaster, it's only six weeks out of your life. If you've been training for ten years, how many six-week periods are there in your training history?

Never mind, I'll answer for you: about 86.

Can you stand to build a better butt from hip thrusts and squatting? Do you need to improve a single weak lift, usually squats or deadlifts? There are countless programs out there. Pick one and follow it.

Show up to the gym with your workout in hand. Have it printed out and folded into your journal. Follow it. Finish it.

3. You're Not Mastering the Basic Lifts

Strive for mastery while you train. Guys, I know you think you impress the girls by loading up the leg press and slamming the weights up and down over and over.

Want to know what they really think of this? I asked them. They think you're an asshole.

Learn to lift correctly. Master squatting deeply. It's easy to find clinics and workshops from the best and brightest on how to move better. In a typical city, there are often several competing workshops on any given weekend.

Your job is to squat deep, bench without the butt leaving the bench and deadlift double bodyweight (at least). The basics are going to get you there the fastest.

And, as a reward, you will be bigger, leaner and stronger.

4. Your Diet is Undoing Your Training

You can't out-cardio countless grams of crappy carbs. I know that vegetables, fruits and quality protein are more expensive than wheat and corn products, but cows get fat by grazing on grain. Don't be a cow.

There are 168 hours in a week. If you train during five of them, that leaves 163 hours to possibly undo anything you achieved in the gym, so how about giving at least a passing nod to eating right?

Learning the basics of cooking—as simple as learning how to use a knife, a slow cooker and a grill, along with some proactive shopping—will do as much for you as the next great "secret" training protocol.

5. You're Wasting Your Rest Periods

Reconsider your definition of rest. I never time rest periods and try to use the time between lifts to do my mobility work, my flexibility work and my correctives.

The problem with gyms today, among other things, is that there are multiple televisions affixed to the walls. Add to that a magical super phone and the dozens of other things that distract us from training, and well...listen, when you're in the gym, train.

And please don't make a mix of your favorite songs. Years ago, I was told the Soviets discovered that "noxious" music actually increased the ability to train. Hey, maybe it was a lie, but I think it's a great idea. If you hate country, listen to country. I hate pop music, so hearing it over the speakers in a public facility makes me train harder. Hate and extreme aggravation are great motivators.

So maybe, instead of reshuffling your "intensity mix," lie on the ground and work that stretch you know you need. Or, as the great bodybuilders used to do, superset most of what you're doing so you never truly rest.

I'm a big fan of supersetting for any sports goal. Obviously, you'd avoid doing this with the Olympic and powerlifts, but try these:

- One-arm press with TRX pulls.
- Curls (any kind) with triceps extensions (any kind).
- Bench press or pushup with rowing.
- Also, squats and swings work well together and make a great metabolic conditioning workout. I enjoy doing ten or fifteen swings and then popping the 'bell up for five goblet squats. Try this for a total of 100–150 swings while listening to the latest crappy pop song.

Bonus Suggestions

- Take the towel off your neck, Rocky.
- There's no reason—ever—for a headband or doo-rag (more like a don't rag. Oh, snap!).
- Wipe off any bench or pad after you use it.
- Put away the weights, even if you didn't leave them lying there.
- Squat in the squat racks. Nothing else.
- Don't scream when doing something that's causing a burn…unless you're literally on fire.
- If you're going to wear a tank top, look more like a tank and less like a tool.
- Be nice to the staff.
- Learn to squat deep. Nothing gives you more gym cred than a deep squat.

The More You Lift, the Worse You Look?

IF I SEE ONE MORE GUY with tribal tats, rolled-up sleeves, and a 145-pound body doing a lat spread in front of a gym mirror, bad things will happen.

Real power and success come from the muscles you DON'T see in the mirror, but little Eddie using his weight belt for curling doesn't know this yet.

I spend a lot of time in gyms. I've been noticing something for a while: some people look worse the more they train. They begin to get the body posture of old age with both arms bent, shoulders pulled far forward and a terrible hitch in their hips. It's the sign of age. It's also the most muscular pose.

And that's the issue.

As we've become more and more a collection of benchers and curlers, we're making ourselves "bent" from our training. As such, I'd like to share a few ideas for you to add to your training to balance out your body and, in the process, look miles better for very little extra effort.

Something's Missing

The day after watching the Winter Olympics in any sport, go out to a local rink or park and watch people attempt the same sport.

Or, watch an NBA game and then watch your neighbors play a pick-up game. Likewise, watch a master chef cut carrots and you'll see the same thing when you flail away with the knife. Keep your fingers out of the soup, please.

Well, what is it that's appealing about those observations?

It's grace. It's elegance. It's beauty.

It might sound odd, but if I were forced to talk about only one issue for those interested in fitness, it would be grace.

I missed a great revolution in track and field. While I was competing, athletes focused on two things: getting stronger and improving technique. Honestly, this is still pretty good advice. Today, a typical track athlete will spend huge amounts of time focusing on posture, position, and the spotting of the eyes. Track practice and ballet work at the barre have more in common than the brutal efforts of my career.

And, to be honest, I'm jealous of this new generation.

Art De Vany brought this to my attention when I first logged onto the internet. He noted that the X look for men was a sign of health. Men, he noted, should have broad shoulders, a thin waist, powerful buttocks and thighs, and not worry about their showy arms. Women, on the other hand, would show fertility with an hourglass figure with a narrow waist "bordered" by a rounder top and bottom.

Images of Raquel Welch in *One Million Years B.C.* can still fire an immediate response in most straight men, and I'm certainly no different.

The X look and the hourglass figure also have a subtle aspect many people miss. For years, as I added more and more bulk to compete at the higher levels of my sport, an interesting thing began to happen: I began to sway as I walked. I began to resemble an ape.

But I didn't walk like one of those elegant apes. My swaying led to some hip problems that led to a knee injury. To undo those years of damage—and this isn't hyperbole, as we're literally talking about decades of poor exercise choices and poor posture—I learned the two keys to a better physique, better performance and happy, pain-free joints.

And, you may well ask, what are the two keys?

Grace and compression.

Now, grace might be apparent to most people (and because of that, sadly ignored), but compression is another issue altogether.

What We Compress, Expands

Not long ago, I had one of those twin-epiphany moments that provided clarity for life. I attended a late-night yoga session and discovered the harder I pulled myself into a position, the more my body responded during the rest period by expanding.

Literally, what we compress, expands.

The next morning, a young teacher noted that having uniforms at school "made no sense." Rather than give her the standard answer of clothes making the person, I said, "What we compress, expands," and walked away.

Later in the day, this young teacher sought me out, thanked me and told me that single line was the most logical insight into teaching she'd ever heard. And, as true as it is for my poor students cramped in tie and jacket, it's even truer for the body.

Grace and compression should live in a yin-yang relationship in fitness goals. When standing for long periods, walking and sprinting or during training, make sure to strive for grace.

When doing restorative work and mobility work, let yourself dance through the "compression and expansion" feeling and be sure not to let either partner lead.

Grace is a remarkable thing. If you make the conscious decision to sit more gracefully, you tend to rise more gracefully. On an odd note, if you decide to throw the discus more gracefully, with a calm elongated head and quiet movements, the discus will thank you by flying farther.

There's an elegance in superior sport and artistic movements that allows even someone completely unfamiliar with the performance to figure out who's the best without having to resort to the box scores.

To get the benefits of compression, you can take a yoga class, join a mobility group, or take a deep study into flexibility. Pavel Tsatousline has a wonderful book, *Relax into Stretch,* where he outlines techniques such as waiting out the stretch, proprioceptive neuromuscular facilitation, isometric stretching, contrast breathing, forced relaxation and, my favorite, The Clasped Knife Technique.

Somehow, comparing stretching to the use of a switchblade seemed to waken something in my interest in learning to stretch at a higher level. Traditional stretching movements are very important in understanding the role of compression. Literally, we squeeze ourselves into positions, then relax and expand.

How much time and effort should you spend in these efforts?

As I tell people time and again, as we age, besides not getting into a serious traumatic accident, there are two things to focus on: hypertrophy (increasing lean body mass) and joint mobility.

Mobility isn't exactly flexibility; it's the easy movement of the body around each joint.

How much time should you spend on hypertrophy and joint mobility? All the time you can spare!

If the goal is to live well enough as long as you can, don't overlook either.

Tonic and Phasic Muscles

Years ago, Vladimir Janda, a Czechoslovakian neurologist and exercise physiologist, began discussing the muscles necessary for posture. To simplify, Janda separated muscles into two groups: tonic, which tend to shorten when tired (or old) and phasic, which tend to weaken under stress (or age).

A simple chart:

Muscles That Get Tighter (Tonic)	Muscles That Get Weaker (Phasic)
Upper Trapezius	*Rhomboids*
Pectoralis Major (Chest)	*Mid-back*
Biceps	*Triceps*
Pectoralis Minor (Deep chest muscle)	*Gluteus Maximus*
Psoas (Those hip flexors that get bad press)	*Deep Abs*
Piriformis	*External Obliques*
Hamstrings	*Deltoids*
Calf Muscles	

I usually explain it this way: if you were chased by a tiger up a tree, the muscles you use to hang on to the branch for a long time are tonic muscles.

If you decided to chase a deer or throw rocks at it, you would use your phasic muscles.

Sadly, most trainers have this backward, they tend to emphasize the "mirror muscles" like the pecs and biceps (bench press and curls), and ignore the muscles that really are the muscles of youth.

Years ago, I had this wonderful conversation with some women in the 100-Pound Club. To be a member, one needed to lose one hundred pounds. Most of them had figured out that all they needed for "the biggest bang for their buck" in terms of weightlifting was to do standing presses and squats.

Looking at the Janda list above, you can see they intuitively understood the need for strengthening the phasic muscles.

But here's the issue: should you go to yoga five days a week for two hours at a time, then drive to the weightroom, and then to the track stadium and train like a track and field athlete?

Well, you could, I guess.

But let me suggest this: Stretch the tonic muscles as efficiently as possible and train the phasic muscles with some level of intensity.

The wonderful thing about all of this is the utter simplicity of doing "all of this."

Goals of This Program

- To develop the "X" look in men and the "hourglass" in women
- Build a platform for grace in movement
- Expand the body through compression (stretching the tonics)
- Build some lean explosive body mass (strengthen the phasics)
- Stretch the tonics

One wonderful thing about the two groups outlined by Janda: they work together in systems. When I do a pec stretch, I also stretch my biceps and a bunch of other wonderful things.

The TRX is a relatively new innovation I've grown to love. I can't get enough of the Skin the Cat one can do by simply leaning out (like a gymnast doing an iron cross) and then rolling the upper body around to loosen up the pecs, biceps and really, everything else too.

Don't have a TRX?

Try Laura Inverarity's inexpensive alternative:

1. Stand in the middle of a doorway with one foot in front of the other.
2. Bend your elbows to a ninety-degree angle and place your forearms on each side of the doorway.
3. Shift your weight onto your front leg, leaning forward until you feel a stretch in your chest muscles.
4. Hold for fifteen seconds.
5. Relax and return to starting position.
6. Repeat ten times.

For stretching the hip flexor, I like Josh Hillis' method:

1. Take the same starting position as a standing lunge.
2. Turn your back heel out, so your back toe points toward your front heel.
3. Push your front knee forward, but keep it behind your toes.
4. Flex your butt hard, like I was going to kick you in the butt.

5. Tilt your hips forward and up (if your hands were on your hips, you would be tilting your hips so your pointer finger pointed up).

I do this movement, along with the goblet squat, every single day of my life. Yes, it's that important to stretch the hip flexors.

For the piriformis, the hamstrings and those wonderfully stiff calves, I strongly suggest rolling them over either a foam roller or "my version" for a roller. I was too cheap to buy a foam roller, so I merely cut up a six-inch PVC pipe when its life as a slosh pipe had expired. I used the hacksaw to make four nice rollers.

Yes, it hurts more than foam. Sorry.

Rolling out these three areas seems to do more good than the kind of static stretching usually prescribed for this kind of issue. If you need more, roll, then stretch.

It's important to note that I'm not giving you an exact step-by-step approach (come to think of it, I don't think that's my role anyway). Instead I'm trying to clue you in to an approach at achieving some balance in your training. If you just add these stretches and the next exercise, many of us would cut back on our chronic issues in our shoulders and hips.

Holy Rhomboids, Batman!

The ONLY muscle I always refer to by name is the rhomboids. As a thrower and lifter for nearly five decades, I've come to appreciate these for their hard work in holding me together. To keep them whole, I do something I call "Bat Wings."

Yes, I invented them...just after I invented the internet.

Lie face down on a standard bench with two dumbbells on the floor. Now here's where it gets confusing...I don't care at all about the range of movement. I only want you to grab those 'bells and squeeze your thumbs up into your armpits, cramming your shoulder blades together. Hold it for ten seconds.

Oh, yes, you did go too heavy, didn't you? Go lighter.

Do this for five to ten "sets."

The next day that really cramped feeling muscle in your upper back is called the rhomboids. Oh, and you're welcome. You see, the development of the rhomboids will save your shoulders, make you stand taller, and lead you to a life of wisdom and wealth. Maybe.

The Single Best Exercise

Now, we come to my favorite four muscles: triceps, deep abs, external obliques and deltoids. These are the muscles that help throwers throw. When I was growing up, these were those that gave us "barn-door delts" and "shoulders like a man!"

The exercise I have for you would be my answer to the question: "If you could only do one exercise what would it be?"

Moreover, if I had to pick the single best lift to teach the athlete and provide lean body mass, my answer would be the same.

I'd choose the one-arm press.

What does it teach? Rooting. Being one piece. Locking down.

It also works a massive number of muscles, and the learning curve is straight up. You can learn the one-arm press in seconds, and master it in just a few workouts.

Any kettlebell-certified trainer can instruct you on the basics in a snap. Really, it's simple, but I'd prefer that you keep an eye on your foot placement. I often do this lift with one foot in the air, just to get a sense of the whole body reacting to the load.

For most workouts, keep your feet narrower than shoulder-width; occasionally do them heel to heel.

As for the movement, be sure to start low (I always touch my thumb on my pec to make sure I'm starting deep enough), and then progress to a total elbow lockout.

Don't lead with the trap by shrugging. I like to squeeze my lat to start the movement. If this is too complex, it's my fault!

Let me try again: take a 'bell, press it overhead.

There!

A Bad Case of Saggy Butt?

Finally, the glutes. Folks, glutes are the image of youthfulness. There was a great episode of *Sex in the City* (yes, I watched it and I liked it!) where one of the girls falls for a very wealthy older man. All goes well until she sees his bad case of saggy butt.

A tight buttocks (I need Goldmember's voice here) is a sign of health and youth. Get one. Preferably yours.

How? As a track coach, I can tell you this: don't underestimate sprinting. Or hill sprinting. Or squatting. Is this too simple?

My idea of sprinting is something I shared online a few years ago:

We usually start with the "great eight" sprints. In the back of my house, there's a long parkway and we do eight build-up sprints. The idea is to start slow, then ease off. Actually, we do try to accelerate through each set, but the goal is to get the sprint work in without hurting anything.

The eight sprints are between forty and sixty meters. We try to accelerate in the middle of each set, increasing the intensity with each sprint.

It's honestly enough for most people. If you have kettlebells, toss in some swings and goblet squats. If you have barbells, do some squats

If you only have machines, fix that.

These tiny additions to your program won't take that much time, but the impact, over time, will be tremendous. While little Eddie is working his "wings," I'll be running hills with Raquel.

High-Performance, No-BS Correctives

CORRECTIVE EXERCISE HAS EXPLODED over the past decade. As with most things in life, we went way too far in one direction, and now the pendulum is swinging back to the point that some are saying it's all "a waste of time."

Corrective efforts can be anything from hands-on work like chiropractor adjustments and massage, to rolling on a lacrosse ball. Of course, it can also be basic stretches or gliding mobility moves. Doing mobility work is important for everyone. Now, telling me that your special brand of mobility work is going to cure cancer or disease (or regulate the ascending colon, as I was told) is a bit suspicious, if not downright idiotic.

Yes, I want to know how to better move my neck, but closing one eye and moving my neck isn't going to cure a necrotic hip, no matter how much you spent on that certification.

I always look for the connections in successful sport programs to see what the best and brightest are doing and simply imitate them, and the same goes with corrective work. The problem is with "enough is enough."

Correction Keys

The key to correction is for the coach to have a toolkit of regressive movements that allow one to de-load and de-stress so they can perform the fundamental movements comfortably and pain free. Safety is part of performance. Putting a weight correctly back on the ground is going to do more for your back health than all the correctives I can teach you after you haphazardly lower the load.

Performance in the weightroom should be like gymnastics—you should be striving for perfection the moment you enter the room.

Basics One: Movements

When it comes to correctives and corrective work, we must first make sure we're dealing with the basics of risk. After that, we have to get a bit smarter. As I always tell people, "Sure, you can do this and that, but what about the rest of us with these things called 'lives'?"

Before you spend two hours a day with your magic wand, get back to the basics, which, in my weightroom, approach strength training from that list of basic human movements (I repeat things until I know you can recite them in your sleep):

- Push
- Pull
- Hinge
- Squat
- Loaded Carry
- The Sixth Movement (basically everything else)

The first step to addressing any corrective work is to find the gaps. If you looked at that list and instantly argued for vertical push versus horizontal push and vertical pull versus horizontal pull but you've never done a deadlift, swing, squat or farmer walk, well, there's your first gap.

I look at it three ways.

First, are you doing each of the basic human movements at least weekly? I argue you should do each of them daily—just the movement for a few reps with a light load. A daily light set of goblet squats will do wonders for hip mobility and the overall squat pattern.

Second, how many total reps are you doing for each movement? For pushes, pulls and squats, I like to see the weekly and monthly numbers to be almost equal. If you do seventy-five presses, do seventy-five squats.

For many, it's wise to increase the number of pulls to undo the damage of years of being too "pushy." Similarly, I argue that you should keep a running list of your exercise variations. If you do dozens of different presses but only one kind of pull, that might slowly become an issue.

Third, do you have some level of balance between your basic human movements? I've come up with lots of small standards. For instance, the power clean, front squat and bench press should all be about the same. This works well for throwers, but not so well for many others.

I don't want to beat on it too much, but a balanced level of strength across all movements tends to keep an athlete healthier.

The movement approach is the first step to correctives—do all the basic human movements and then balance the total reps and total load as well as you can.

Basics Two: Muscles

From there we can take a global look at correctives by looking at the muscles. For that, we have to look at life and living. If there are rules, here they are:

- Most adults need to strengthen the phasics and stretch the tonics.
- Next, deal with a lifetime of asymmetry issues.
- Finally, deal with too much sitting and not moving.

As Theodor Hettinger made clear in *Physiology of Strength* (written in the early 1950s), the phasic muscles—the glutes, deltoids, triceps, and abs—are also the muscles that tend to respond quickest to strength training.

The tonic muscles—chest, biceps, psoas, etc.—are often overtrained in many settings. Bench press, curl and lat pulldown workouts tend to tighten the muscles that need to be stretched back toward normal. The modern gym with its myriad of seated machines lock that poor tight hip flexor and hamstring into the same place it's been all day while sitting, driving, typing and, in general, not moving.

Janda came up with his two classifications based on those that tend to shorten when tired (tonic) and those that tend to weaken under stress or age (phasic).

Athletes make a Faustian deal when entering into the world of sports, as it's a rare sport that doesn't end up causing massive asymmetries. Elite sports demand world-class strength at the cost of ignoring other weaknesses and issues.

Over time, performance improves because of this focus, but it leads to long-term issues. Randy Matson, former world record holder in the shot put, was once asked if he still threw. He answered, "I can barely pick up my brief case with my right hand."

That's the deal with the devil elite athletes make to get to the top.

As such, we need to address the weakening and tightening of nature plus the effects of life, sports and everything else when we address corrective work. Corrective work should be seamless with the entire program. I strongly discourage trainers and coaches from having a mobility section of training, a flexibility part and a corrective part.

If because of injury, trauma or life, you can't do the big movements (bench press, deadlift, squat and the Olympic lifts), you should step back and do even more basic moves. These are regressions, and regressions are the best correctives.

Regressions

Recently I had a group of elite Navy personnel doing pelvic tilts—or hip thrusts—for sets of twenty-five. The next day, the head of the group told me, "From now on, I'm doing these—alone, mind you, but I'm doing these."

Hip thrusts are a one-stop shop for stretching the hip flexors, building the butt and providing an insight about how we cheat on butt work in general (a condition characterized by Janda as "gluteal amnesia"). We need to get on the ground and squeeze those cheeks together.

Under load, you certainly may call these "hip thrusts." I'm very interested in the work of Bret Contreras and Nick Horton in showing people the value of this movement not only for show, but also for go. Nick's Olympic lifters are using the hip thrust as a basic training move and are making great progress.

This movement is what I call a regression, and please don't discount any of these. Use every one you can in general warmups or, as I prefer, during rest periods from other movements. These will keep the heart rate up and make sure things go well for you.

Of the five fundamental human movements (push, pull, hinge, squat and loaded carries), the one that typically needs the most regressions is the squat.

Three Squat Regressions

My regressions for the squat are as follows:

a. *Six-Point Rocking.* The six-point position is on hands, knees and feet. From there, squat butt to heels. There you go. Widen the knees as you wish, but this is the basic move. If you can do this and still can't squat, load is the issue. You need to learn to squat between the legs, which leads to the next regression.

b. *Doorknob Drill.* Stand arms length from a doorknob or partner. Grab the handle or partner's hands with both hands and puff your chest "up"—imagine being on a California beach when a swimsuit model walks by, which tightens the lower back and locks the whole upper body. The lats will naturally spread a bit and the shoulders will come back a little. Continue with the arms in the "hammer throwing" position (hands grabbing the doorknob), the Muscle Beach chest, and then lean back away from the door.

c. *Goblet Squat.* You know this one: With a weight cradled against your chest, squat down and let the elbows slide past the inside of your knees.

Goblet squats are all the squatting many people need. What people discover at this instant is a basic physiological fact—the legs are not stuck like stilts under the torso; rather, the torso is slung between the legs. As you go down, leaning back with arms straight, you'll discover one of the true keys of lifting: you squat between your legs.

To determine stance, I often just have the person jump two or three times. Note the landing position on jumps two and three. Have the person look at the heel to toe alignment. That's the stance. A touch wider or a touch narrower— it takes a few tries, but it's fairly natural.

If someone can six-point rock and do the doorknob drill, the goblet squat is usually just a few reps away.

To summarize the goblet squat:

1. Sit between the legs
2. Minimize shin movement
3. Keep a big chest and a big arch in the back

Done correctly, squats may be the only exercise needed for success in sports.

Teaching Points for the Three Squat Regressions

Six-Point Rock

- Down on hands and knees
- Crush grapes in the armpits
- Grip the ground (don't let the pads of the fingertips come off the ground)
- Gently "rock" or squat horizontally "up and down"

Doorknob Drill
- Butt back and knees out
- Shins stay vertical
- Drive through the heels and straight up (pretend there's a glass of wine on your head)

Goblet Squat
- Drop down and aim the elbows for the insides of the knees
- Push the knees out with the elbows
- Get a big chest
- Drive through the heels and come straight up (don't let the hips shoot up first)

You can add corrective work between sets of any exercise. My rest periods are now almost entirely devoted to stretching the tonic muscles or working on a skill. The basic regressions you can apply today are:

For the push: Planks

For the pull: TRX or suspension work (especially one-arm rows)

For the hinge: Pelvic tilts or hip thrusts

For the squat: Squat regressions listed above

For loaded carries: The farmer walk teaches the key concepts of lifting (tall posture, shoulders packed, pelvis in line, solid grip)

Tonic Time

I'm a huge fan of progressive resistance, but we must also keep our eyes on the quality of movement. I work corrective movement, all of it from foam rolling to regressions, into the basic training program.

An area of training that most ignore is the concept of tonic workouts. These are training days where you go into the gym and move a lot but don't stress anything. It's simple—you go to the gym and do a workout with your normal moves but with fairly light weights. If you're experienced, forty percent is a fun number to train with here.

Now, I actually suggest doing these at home so you can just get the movements done and just feel good. On this type of day, increase the amount of stretching, foam rolling and other tissue work. I often recommend increasing this to two days a week, especially when doing a high-volume squat routine. Those who squat heavy and often understand the odd kind of soreness that brings.

Brilliant at the Basics

If I had an empty schedule and unlimited time to train, I'd love to throw every corrective exercise and soft tissue modality at my old body and see how supple I could get. The fact is, no one has that kind of time or patience, nor is it even necessary.

Take it from me: regressions are the best corrections.

Rebuild Yourself with Complexes

IF I EVER RECOMMENDED A WORKOUT that cut fat and built muscle at the same time, I'm not sure I'd believe myself. After all the late-night television hucksters, I don't know what to believe anymore.

And, yet, here I am. Complexes might just be the answer to the great riddle of the Strength Sphinx: how can we cut fat and build muscle at the same time?

It All Started When...

After eight years in a Catholic elementary school, I moved on to a public junior high school and discovered how sheltered my life had been. Southwood Junior High in South San Francisco was a far cry from the quiet confines of my parish school with the good Irish nuns.

One thing we did have at Southwood was a fabulously simple weight training program.

Our Southwood workout was very straightforward:

> *Power clean × 8-6-4*
> *Military press × 8-6-4*
> *Front squat × 8-6-4*
> *Bench press × 8-6-4*

On one particular day, due to a short class period for an assembly, our instructor, Mr. Freeman, simplified things even more. We just had to do power cleans, military presses and front squats for eight reps followed by a short rest as we alternated with our partners. Then we'd do them for six reps before finishing with four.

Without the bench press, this workout sounded easy. He added one little thing, though: You couldn't put the bar down once you started the three lifts.

It's the back-to-back brutality that adds up, my friends. I choked on those last reps of the front squat trying to figure out where I left my lungs.

From an earlier chapter, you'll remember the idea behind complexes and how valuable they can be. That assembly day was my first complex and where I learned that important lesson.

Going Back in Time

The roots of complexes are fairly deep. Complexes reflect the peripheral heart action (PHA) workouts pioneered in the 1960s by Mr. America, Bob Gajda, who also assisted the legendary Sergio Olivia. You can find more about PHA in John McCallum's book *Keys to Progress*.

Here's an example of one sequence from a PHA workout:

> *Front squat × 12*
> *Cuddle situps × 25*
> *Curls × 10*
> *Seated twists × 25*
> *Wrestler's bridge × 10*

Then rest and repeat the sequence four total times. You'd then do up to three or four other sequences during this workout. PHA had advantages, as it seemed to burn a lot of fat and covered every body part imaginable.

There's an obvious problem with PHA. You have to have a lot of equipment, and it would be nice to be able to move from dumbbell to barbell to chinup bar without having to wait or find the stuff you just left behind a minute ago. Those of us who have trained in college gyms or public establishments know that equipment will literally walk away to another corner as you move from exercise to exercise.

For many of us who trained in the 1970s, the Universal Gym was the answer to this problem. I had football workouts that were just this:

> *Bench press*
> *Lat pulldown*
> *Leg press*
> *Hyperextension*
> *Leg extension and leg curl*
> *Neck harness*
> *Wrist roller*
> *Shoulder press*
> *Incline situp*

After thirty seconds at each station, the coach would blow the whistle. We'd move to the next station and continue training. This workout could accommodate a lot of athletes and, for what is was, it was a good workout.

The Nautilus machine workouts were also believed to improve cardiovascular condition by quickly moving from station to station. It also allowed the gym owners to shuttle clients out of the gym pretty fast, too.

Complexes, the Javorek Way

In past years, Istvan "Steve" Javorek's work with complexes has been stolen and repackaged many times. I have to make a short nod to something he notes on his website:

> *"From what I've heard, from the far end of Siberia to Iceland to California, thousands of coaches are performing with their athletes Javorek's Complex exercises, but some of them give credit to themselves. I really worked hard on developing these exercises and I like to share with everyone my 'little secrets,' just give credit to the 'creator.'*

> *"My original goal with the complex exercises was to find an efficient and aggressive method of performance enhancement that saves time and makes the program more enjoyable. If you choose to use these (in some form) with your athletes, be honest and call your new complex exercises 'Variation to Javorek's Complex Exercises.'"*

Javorek's complexes are brilliant and have all the keys to success for someone contemplating them:

Javorek's Barbell Complex One

Barbell upright row × 6
Barbell high-pull snatch × 6
Barbell behind-the-head squat and push press × 6
Barbell behind-the-head good morning × 6
Barbell bent-over row × 6

More Complexes, More Pain

Alwyn Cosgrove is another master of the complex. After the Velocity Diet those years ago, I began doing Alwyn's Afterburn II program and soon discovered that doing complexes on their own was one of the biggest oversights in my training career. Alwyn's insights include one variation for the busy person that I'll address in a moment.

My definition of a complex is simple. A complex is a series of lifts back to back where you finish the reps of one lift before moving on to the next lift. The barbell only leaves your hand or touches the floor after all of the lifts are complete. Although you can do them with dumbbells or kettlebells, I argue that we only use barbells. Certainly, there's great value in the other tools, but for getting athletes bigger, I like to use the heavier bar.

The key to organizing a complex is to make sure the bar passes over your head in some kind of logical manner. In other words, if you do rows followed by back squats, how did the bar get back there? I try to have the bar pass backward over the head after a few lifts, but only pass forward again once.

When you try these, it's probably best to use a broomstick first. It'll save some effort if you think about the exercise transitions before you get too heavy.

For example, if you have a military press before a back squat, on the last military press rep, lower the weight to the back.

Take a minute to think things through before going for a max on these complexes.

Your rest periods should be longer than what you originally think. Like most of my workouts, these appear easy on paper.

The most difficult thing to consider is the rep range. For a fat-burning hit and a massive conditioning bang, try doing sets of eight:

Complex A for Eights

Row × 8
Clean × 8
Front squat × 8
Military press × 8
Back squat × 8
Good mornings × 8

Gently place the bar on the ground and rest!

I like sets of three for adding mass to my young athletes. The more time under the bar, the more the body adapts by getting bigger. Moreover, it seems to also be most helpful on the playing field. When you watch a sophomore handle Complex A with 155 for three complexes of three reps each, you realize this is a very strong human being, even if he's just fifteen.

You can play with any rep variations you like, but I've found that eights and threes are the best. If you do five sets of eight, you probably won't be doing much more in this workout. Three sets of three make an excellent pre-lift warmup or, with heavier weights, can be used as a strength and mass-building workout.

The sets seem to be almost geometric in their impact on the body. Err on the side of caution for the first few workouts before attempting more than three sets in the complexes.

Alwyn adds another variation I use for strength building, which is this: drop a rep each set and add weight. Now, be careful here, as the weights go up quickly.

Let's look at Complex C with this variation:

Complex C

Hang snatch

Overhead squat

Back squat

Good mornings

Row

Deadlift

Set 1: 8 reps with the bar, 45 pounds

Set 2: 7 reps with 65 pounds

Set 3: 6 reps with 85 pounds

Set 4: 5 reps with 105 pounds

Set 5: 4 reps with 125 pounds

Set 6: 3 reps with 145 pounds

Set 7: 2 reps with 165 pounds

Set 8: 1 rep with 185 pounds

Now, there's an assumption here that you can snatch 185, then complete the workout. Again, on paper, this looks easy.

One other thing I like to do is to print each complex in size sixty-eight Arial font so we can see the whole series on the ground in front of us. Place the sheet about three feet in front of the barbell and keep your mind on the exercise at hand, using the sheet to remind you to move to the next exercise. With large groups, I have the sheets in plastic protectors, and we use them for weeks before they get torn.

The Select Six

Now it's time I offer you my six favorite complexes. Note that each has six lifts and many of the exercises will be familiar. And my reminder: if you don't know how to do a lift, don't do it. Find yourself a coach and get help.

Complex A

Row
Clean
Front squat
Military press
Back squat
Good mornings

Complex B

Deadlift
Clean-grip high pull
Clean-grip snatch
Back squat
Good mornings
Row

Complex C

Hang snatch
Overhead squat
Back squat
Good mornings
Row
Deadlift

Complex D

Upright row
Clean-grip snatch
Back squat
Behind-the-neck press
Good mornings
Row

Complex E

Power clean
Military press
Back squat
Good mornings
Behind-the-neck press
Front squat

Complex F

Overhead squat
Back squat
Good morning
Front squat
Rows
Deadlift

Complexes: Keep It Simple

I find that swimming through these three times a week eliminates boredom. If you only do them twice a week and play with the three reps schemes (eights, threes and 8-7-6-5-4-3-2-1), you have eighteen workout ideas to last nine weeks.

When I sell this on late night TV, I'll be the guy with the ponytail and spandex.

Ten Simple Tips to Get More Mass

SOMETIMES PEOPLE JUST DON'T GET IT. Or, and I'm beginning to think this is happening more often, they simply don't have the tools to "get it."

I was standing with my assistant coach at a track meet and one of our runners was clearly floundering. It's not uncommon to watch someone who's underprepared and out of condition to flounder in the 400-meter sprint. Well, "sprint" is a bit of stretch in this example, but as he came by, one of his teammates yelled, "Don't give up!" I turned to my assistant and said, "Was it over when the Germans bombed Pearl Harbor?"

One of my athletes turned to us and said, in that sarcastic tone that God graces adolescents whenever they feel superior, "Coach, that was the Japanese."

Right. Except I was quoting one of the finest films of all time, *Animal House,* which belongs in the pantheon of Great Films along with *Groundhog Day, Fight Club* and *The Godfather.* Somewhere, John Belushi groaned.

The point is, some people just don't have the tools to get it, and that's the issue most people face when they try to gain mass.

There are real problems with the mass-gain program. I expect you to do high-rep squats. I expect you to do complexes. I expect you to get stronger. Nowhere did I say it would be fun. And yet, many fail on this goal of building more mass.

Let's add some tools to the tool kit to get you going again.

1. Rethink the Week

There's a chance, especially if you're six feet tall or even just long-limbed, that you simply can't handle the number of times a week that traditional mass-building programs require. You need to rethink the week. Now, I was there for the first week and I clearly voiced my opinion that for hypertrophy training, taller guys should have a ten-day week, but God had other plans.

Change your week into a three-week pattern. For people who are honestly struggling in the gym for muscle gain but failing to see any, let's consider training after two days of rest ALL of the time. It's easy to follow over three weeks:

	Week One	Week Two	Week Three
Monday	Train	Rest	Rest
Tuesday	Rest	Rest	Train
Wednesday	Rest	Train	Rest
Thursday	Train	Rest	Rest
Friday	Rest	Rest	Train
Saturday	Rest	Train	Rest
Sunday	Train	Rest	Rest

The pattern then repeats. If you're doing those high-rep-squat workouts, it's very difficult to train three times a week. I experimented with training twice a week after a discussion with the late Goran Swenson after he found that Tuesday and Saturday workouts were really helping him stay stronger, longer. That might be worth a look, too, so try both options a few times and see if you begin growing again.

2. Learn to Stop

One of the most overlooked aspects of muscle-building programs is a four-letter word: STOP. Stop playing basketball. Stop jogging. Stop doing cardio. I swear, if I get one more email like this, I will do something rash:

"Hey, Dan:

I'm interested in doing Highland Games. I want to put on some weight, but I have MMA classes three days a week, play in two basketball leagues and I want to do a marathon. What lifts should I do to put on sixty pounds?"

I tell you, that's NOT an exaggeration. It's not.

Learn to walk slowly. Learn to lie down. Learn to nap. I have argued my whole coaching career that the single hardest thing to do is to add quality lean muscle mass.

Now, I didn't say "weight" as the people with the Big Gulps and doughnuts have bravely shown us. I said lean muscle mass.

3. Get Lean, Then Gain Mass

One person in a hundred will have the courage to listen to my best piece of advice to prep for a mass-building program: lean out first.

My buddy in college who decided to enter an amateur bodybuilding contest lived for a month on nothing but lettuce and dope. Yes, you read that right, and no, don't try it. For his last workouts, his friends had to literally pull him off the floor to do anything. The loads on the bar were far, far below his normal training numbers. But under the posing lights, he looked marvelous.

A funny thing happened the weeks and months after the contest: the guy exploded. It was like he was being inflated. He gained size in all the right places, seemingly every day.

I know there's a scientific explanation for this, but I don't care what it is. The same thing happened to me after the Velocity Diet. A week later, I lifted in an open Olympic lifting meet, and everyone swore I had put on ten pounds of muscle, but I was actually two pounds lighter.

If you have the courage to lean out, try it!

4. Take Creatine

If you choose to lean out first, I've some good news for you: creatine works. Try it for three weeks and don't overload yourself with it. Take the recommended dose and don't get into the mindset (actually, it's the "mine-set" because I'm the world's worst offender of "if a little is good, a lot is wonderful!") of needing to load it. Coming off a period of leaning out, creatine seems to "supercharge" itself as you start eating normal and training hard.

An interesting observation, though: I've noticed that guys who start pouring creatine into their drinks without leaning out first or without any rhyme or reason to using the supplement often get little back from it.

If you're going to use it, think it through a bit. The lab coats go to the trouble of printing a recommended dosing strategy on the label; follow it.

5. Have a Plan before You Go In

You need to up the workout intensity. In college, I became "famous," as the local radio and newspapers mentioned repeatedly, for drinking cold coffee and eating a grapefruit before competing. Two things: first, I didn't normally drink coffee, so I got a bit of a buzz from it, and, two, I'd read somewhere that something in the grapefruit made the caffeine work better. There was probably some truth in that, but whatever it takes to get you going, take it!

Ingest whatever you think is appropriate—there are many options at the local gas station to "give you a buzz." While you're waiting for it to kick in, do one more thing: write out EXACTLY what you hope to accomplish during the workout. If you're going to take 225 for a set of twenty-five back squats, then rest and do another twenty, write that down.

If there has been one tiny change in my training that has helped the most, it's writing down my plan for my training before I begin. Try it.

6. Take Fish Oil

Do I have to write this? Honestly? Ahem, here goes: are you taking fish oil? Because, if you're not, you have totally missed the last decade of research. Fish oil capsules are so inexpensive and work so well that I can't believe some people still don't take them.

How hard is it to pop a couple capsules into your mouth and swallow them? Keep them in your desk, in the bathroom, in the kitchen or wherever you pass by every day. If there's a miracle supplement for both fat loss and muscle gain, this might be it. True, our ancient caveman hunter-gatherer brothers and sisters didn't need fish oil, as they ate the bone marrow and all the organs of an animal, but you do.

7. Stay Warm to Get Big

I thought Dick Notmeyer was crazy (and he may be anyway) when he told me to stay warm when I was trying to get bigger. He suggested keeping a sweatshirt on at the gym, to wear sweaters and jackets and not letting myself get cold. This is old-school advice, folks, but some of the research on shivering and brown fat might support this idea.

If your body is trying to let you get a little bigger, but you insist on shivering, freezing and shaking, the body is going to shift resources to producing heat. Maybe this is pure fluff, but it's easy enough to try.

Think of it this way: while those 142-pound geeks are walking around with their wife-beater shirts, tribal tats and shaved arms, you can be like that Arnold guy who used to keep an air of mystery about him.

8. Really Learn to Squat

It might be worth the effort BEFORE embarking on a mass-building program to take some time to master the squat. Just do it.

9. When in Doubt, Eat More Protein

Again, do I need to tell you to take more protein? If there was a single great lesson from my experience on the Velocity Diet, it was this: I don't get enough protein. I've read many arguments against this point, but my experience and my coaching have underscored this point. It can be in shakes, post-workout drinks, meat, fish, more eggs or whatever, but get more protein! Please.

10. Get Real before You Get Big

Some readers won't like this, but the last tool is a reality check. It's true, under the direction of Dick Notmeyer and a lot of puberty, I put on forty pounds in four months. But I didn't put on much more for three years!

Mass-building programs need to be done on a massive offensive. Line up the bombers and tanks and cannons and blast away!

Then, move back to a basic program again. Six weeks of honest mass building can do wonders; I can't imagine trying that for six years. Two to three times a year, throw yourself full on into a mass-building program. Learn from each attempt and try to remember those lessons for next time.

Bluto says, "And it ain't over now. 'Cause when the goin' gets tough…the tough get goin'! Who's with me? Let's go!"

The Forty-Day Program

FOR THE RECORD, I'm pretty much done with it. I'm tired of hearing about the incredible number of pullups or Hindu pushups people have done for three months while inexplicably failing to gain any appreciable muscle. Worse yet, these fine people email me, asking what they're doing wrong.

Of course, you know my only question.

What are your goals?

The answer, almost universally, is to lose fat and gain some muscle. So, why, I think to myself, are they doing a half-baked high school PE regimen designed from boot camp programs for wars nearly seventy-five years ago? It's one thing to train a depression-era farm boy into an infantryman or Marine, but it was never the drill sergeant's goal to prepare you for a photo shoot on the beach.

The problem with this boot camp approach is that it's been key-holed into what appears to be a modern and scientific training approach for elite training. When you read that the Soviets or East Germans developed these secret techniques in some secret facility in some secret location, hell, I get all 007 too.

Sadly, for most of us, it's just not working.

Let's look at this approach and I'll offer the great insight of this program: the development of qualities.

Quality Development

There were believed to be three stages one went through for elite performance in a sport. Really, I should have an exclamation point after "sport," because that's the point most people miss: If you aren't doing this for a sport, usually an individual sport that's part of the Olympics, none of this is going to be important. But follow along, please.

The stages were:

- General physical preparation (GPP)
- Specialized physical preparation (SPP)
- Competitive period

If you were born after 1964, none of this has been used in your lifetime. While many trainers embrace these three steps as set in stone, and it certainly has great value even if I'm probably too critical, elite athletes have moved to far more specialization.

Of course, as John Jerome wrote years ago, "Specificity works, but at a price." The price for me has been, at best, a lot of limping and, at worst, a lot of surgeries.

The lessons of accumulation are probably what most people mean when they talk about general physical preparation, but let's discuss these older views of training.

GPP is all about building whatever "qualities" are important for a sport. Hang on here, this is important.

SPP is attempting to continue upon the measurements that define the qualities of the sport, but now we attempt to hone skills specific to the sport.

Competition is fairly obvious. It's an attempt to master the skills of a sport during the time of competition. The qualities built upon for the past year or years may or may not support success and that, as I often tell athletes, is the tragedy of this brand of training.

The skill aspects, which I'm going to ignore after this, relate solely to that sport. If you can barely stand up from a chair, but can toss a shot put over seventy-five feet, you're the best shot putter in the world and nobody is going to ask about your heart rate. Every second you walked on the treadmill to get your cardio was time away from building yourself into a champion shot putter.

What are the "qualities?" You can come up with your own list, but let's put out the basics:

> *Strength (the ability to move loads)*
> *Power (the ability to move a load pretty quickly)*
> *Flexibility and joint mobility*
> *Endurance (whatever that means)*
> *Fat loss (if applicable to the sport or goals)*
> *Hypertrophy (if applicable to the sport or goals)*

Obviously, skill shows up in much of any training. Something as simple as speed training can involve lots of deadlifts and squats, but there's also a need for smooth and efficient technique too. I'd argue genetics is where we start when it comes to elite sprinting.

Here's the issue: For most, what qualities are we addressing?

Recently, a bodybuilding magazine stated something along these lines: "We don't want to be strong; we just want to look strong." After I vomited a little in my mouth, I thought about it. It's true. Guys who tell me "I just want to look good naked"—and I pray they aren't thinking of doing that with me—are probably thinking along those lines.

Of course, and I love to point this out, most guys who train to look good naked have to be nearly naked before you can tell they even train. In street clothes, they look like members of the high school band, which is probably why most of them wear T-shirts three sizes too small and cut the sleeves off of most of their clothes.

In other words, the two qualities that the bulk of us wish to achieve nearly all of the time are:

1. *Fat loss*
2. *Hypertrophy (more muscle mass or size, but with an eye toward symmetry)*

Quality: Fat Loss

With perhaps just a nod to the two-week Atkin's diet induction, there's no better plan for fat loss than the Velocity Diet. I went from 249 (or 251 depending on how I stood on the scale that day) to 226 in twenty-eight days. My blood profiles improved so much that my doctor kept flipping the results and shaking his head.

Hear me: The twenty-eight-day Velocity Diet is the best route for fat loss.

Still, I'm also honest. Many people fail on the V-Diet. Day one is tough, but days two through six are brutal. Yes, it eases after week two, but it's never easy.

But, it accomplishes the single most common goal for people when they ask me for advice in diet and training.

I strongly urge you to consider the Alpo Diet as part of your reward and punishment if you embark on a strict diet. Oh, the Alpo Diet? If you fail the diet, you have to eat a can of Alpo in front of your friends. Hell, make a movie and put it on the 'net and let me watch it, too. If you can't help but eat a doughnut, smell some Alpo and think about promise.

The problem with these two qualities—fat loss and hypertrophy—is that so much has been written on them that most people have lost sight of the keys. When people think fat loss, in many cases the first idea is to do massive amounts of crunches, which one world famous bodybuilder told me is the key to getting back surgery in the future.

The answer, then, to most people's goals is to go on the V-Diet or something along those lines. As always, I'm fine with whatever serious approach you take, either the V-Diet or the Atkins induction or the Warrior diet or whatever, but fat loss is diet. Sorry. The truth will set you free, but you will crave doughnuts.

Folks, the V-Diet will find your six-pack. Mine was there under a nice padding of insulation.

Quality: Hypertrophy

As a strength coach, I field a lot of questions about hypertrophy. Actually, against all public opinion to the contrary, hypertrophy is an important part of the game for many sports.

Mike Ditka, a great American football coach, noted on the radio show *Mike and Mike in the Morning* that, "Some guys look good in the shower but can't play." I always say: "Looks like Tarzan, plays like Jane."

We have to be careful with the balance of things.

One way I address this issue is by changing the term "hypertrophy" or "bodybuilding" to "armor building."

Yep, armor.

I played varsity football for South City High back in the glory days (key Bruce Springsteen), and all our games were at night. My last game was played on Thanksgiving, early in the morning. Hours later, when I normally would've been asleep, we ate Thanksgiving dinner. I was amazed at how much pain my upper arms felt from the banging of the game. I didn't realize how many collisions I had in a typical game. And, I don't think I realized that my forearms took most of the beating.

Since that time, I've bought into the idea of armor building for football.

There's no question that the more time one spends under load, the more hypertrophy will result.

But I never give absolutes here. I had an athlete ask about soreness and I found myself speechless, as I've never found any credible evidence that soreness is an indicator of anything. Like soreness, any and all methods of training seem to work across the spectrum, but few of us have ever found the answer that works for everybody every time.

So, how do we increase the amount of time under load?

Earlier in the book I discussed the idea of complexes. Like the circuit training programs of the 1960s, the downside for most people is that we (and I'm including all of us) come into hypertrophy programs too weak. When most people begin doing complexes or circuits or whatever, the weights are too light.

To build muscle, most of us need to build strength. Stability, mobility, and then strength should be the mantra for most of us in weight training.

And it's far simpler than I ever imagined. Recently, I increased my thick-bar deadlift from 265 (this is a seriously thick thick bar) to 315 pounds. I also used this same program to match my best bench press in a decade without going hard for even one workout.

What is this miracle? Well, give me forty days.

The Forty-Day Workout

A few years ago, Pavel Tsatsouline gave me a program. Be wary, this program is so simple you may ignore its value.

1. For the next forty workouts, do the exact same training program every day. For the record, I find most of my goals are reached by day twenty or twenty-two, so you can also opt for a shorter period.

2. Pick five exercises. I suggest a squatting movement like the goblet squat or the overhead squat as part of the warmup, as you don't want to ignore the movement, but it might be fun to focus on other aspects of the body too.

3. Focus on these five movements:

   - A large posterior chain movement (the deadlift is the right answer).
   - Upper body push (bench press, incline bench press, military press).
   - Upper body pull (pullups, rows, or, if you've ignored them like I did, heavy biceps curls).
   - A simple full-body explosive move (kettlebell swings or snatches).
   - And something for an "anterior chain" move (an abdominal exercise). The ab wheel is king here, but you can also do some movements best suited for lower reps.

4. Only do two sets of five reps per workout for the deadlift and the push and pull exercises and one set of twenty to fifty for the explosive move. Do a solid single set of five reps for the abs.

5. Never plan or worry about the weight or the load. Always stay within yourself and go heavy "naturally."

6. Don't eat chalk, scream or pound on walls. Just do each lift without any emotion or excitement, and strive for perfect technique.

The workout might consist of these exercises:

Thick bar deadlift
Bench press
Heavy biceps curls
Kettlebell swings
Ab wheel

In fact, this is exactly what I recently used in my workouts. I often did this five days a week and found that my lifts naturally waved up and down throughout the week and the full forty days. Sometimes, something like a 250-pound bench press would feel so light for both sets of five that I had to hold back on the excitement to do more sets and reps.

The secret to the program is that you get volume from doing up to ten sets of a lift in a week, and the load increases as you naturally feel like the weights are easy.

The first time I tried this program, I added fifteen pounds to my lifetime incline bench press during the twenty-first workout, approximately a month after starting the program. I did this max with no spotter and I got the lift for a double. It was a fifteen-pound improvement over my lifetime best, with an extra rep as a parting gift without doing a single hard workout—just two sets of five anytime I entered the gym.

You can certainly come up with your own variations, but try to stick with the basic five movements and don't stray far from two sets of five. You'll be amazed at how quickly your strength will improve after just a few weeks.

Also, notice the element of randomness in this workout.

With a home gym, I can train this program daily, but I naturally find I take days off here and there because of the nature of life. You could do all forty (or twenty) days in a row, but things will come up.

After finishing all forty days or when you feel your strength has come up to a level that more advanced training methods are appropriate, feel free to move along. The short time you invest in focusing on strength building will do wonders for muscle mass as you begin to attack supersets or whatever you next deem important.

The Forty-Day Workout might be an excellent way to progress through the V-Diet, or any other diet strategy that involves a set number of weeks. After ending the twenty-eight days of the diet, one's strength will take off as you ease off the strict nutritional efforts.

Quick Recap

If the two qualities you want to address are fat loss and hypertrophy, why are you doing all that other nonsense?

Fat loss is diet. I think the Velocity Diet is the best, but I also found amazing success with the Atkins induction. Although you shouldn't ignore exercise, focus on the diet side for fat loss.

For many of the people I've worked with on hypertrophy, basic strength needs to be addressed before we move the program into something more complex. Try the Forty-Day Workout and drive the basic lifts up.

For most of us, our goals will be reached much quicker and relatively easier by a focused diet and a simpler lifting program.

The Olympic Lifts: A Study of Compromises to Options

LATELY I'VE BEEN TALKING A LOT about "managing options" versus "managing compromises." Get used to it. It is the secret to coaching, parenting and management in general.

The sport of Olympic lifting offers a real-time look at how a simple rule change can turn a sport on its ear. There are times in history when we can look back and wonder in amazement how a problem just up and disappeared one day.

As Bill Bryson notes in *Home,* city planners were at their wits' ends a century ago, trying to come up with intelligent ways to deal with the horse poop problem that was vexing every city in the world. The tons of manure created by these engines of industry were making city life a nightmare and yet, a century later most of us probably didn't even know this was an issue. The truck and the car don't leave droppings.

In the same way, before 1972 O lifters regularly complained about their mid-backs. There were also a lot of complaints about the officiating too.

211

Now, you can wonder, "How can there be problems with an O lift? Either you make it or you miss it!"

The issue swirled around the first of the three lifts, the military press. Almost on a monthly basis, someone would figure out a new way to lean, pop, bend or slide down to increase the load by a few more pounds. Some officials would agree and others would give a red light, a missed attempt. But, if two of the three officials liked it, we had a new record.

Where a lifter lived and who the judging officials were changed the way lifters approached their attempts. In addition, all the leaning backward was paying hell on the backs of lifters. So, in a bout of rare wisdom, the fathers of Olympic lifting dropped the movement: the O lifts became the snatch and the clean and jerk, no military press. Meets finished in record time and the quick-lift records shot through the roof.

And the sport all but vanished from the imagination of most people. True, a Vasily or a Naim might come along to make the cover of a larger sport magazine on occasion, but, by and large, the sport disappeared.

An interesting subplot, just for the historians: there was an argument to replace the standing military press with the bench press. Let me say this, and I have to be right because it's impossible to prove otherwise: if O lifting would have added the bench press, there would practically be NO powerlifting (squat, bench press and deadlift competitions), minimal Strongman stuff, and Highland Games would still be more festive than competitive.

But, the international body dropped the press.

What also dropped, and here's the point: before 1972, O lifting was a sport of managing compromises. At a meet, although it was still true that to a point it favors the shorter person in the weight class, one needed enough absolute strength to crush a press, enough power to pull in all three moves, enough flexibility and mobility to handle a crushing load under ballistic conditions, and survive and thrive and, and, and.

Today, there are basically two schools of O lifting: one, the Bulgarian "Butcher" approach as it was described to me at the USOC, where the lifters do the competitive movements heavy and hard several times a day, or, two, the Chinese or German method where you find the lifters doing the competitive movements heavy and hard with some assistance work.

Yes, the Iranian heavies trained a little different and I am sure my brothers and sisters in O lifting will call me all kinds of names for making the point so simple.

Olympic lifting today is all about managing options. Today, selection based on genetics is probably as clear-cut in O lifting as it is in basketball. After genetics, the training environment will be the same in Russia, China, Iran or Greece. The training program is going to be hard to discern differences too.

In my workshops, I always note that O lifting is a Quadrant Four activity, as there are very few qualities, but the relative level of absolute human maximum will astound us. Most people, for example, can't deadlift the weight that's the world record in their weight class in the clean and jerk. Honestly, that could also be said about the snatch, as I hold the double-bodyweight deadlift as a basic standard for competence, and that's a given in the snatch world records.

Life as a football coach means managing compromises. Every few decades, God grants a blue-chip, can't-miss, one-of-a-kind superstar. Enjoy it, by the way.

The question is this: how many times do you give him the ball? I had a coach once tell me about a great athlete he had who scored one out of six times he touched the ball. The question would be: why didn't you give him the ball more? If he's so good, why ever take him out?

Managing compromises. If you leave him in the whole game, he gets tired, banged up and hurt. Giving him the ball every time will give the defense a pretty good shot at stopping him.

So, how much rest? How many times do you fake it? This is game management at its hardest.

Corporations deal with this all the time: this ad we made was very funny. Think of the herding cats commercial of years ago, which was funny and delightful, and we remember it well. What was the name of the company?

"Where's the beef?"
"I can't believe I ate the whole thing."
"We try harder."

When does the funny ad become a tired cliché?

How do you insure the message sells what you produce? That's the compromise.

I often tell people the problem with high school seniors isn't senioritis; rather, for the first time in life (and for some the last), the students face a "managing compromise" situation.

Oh, you can say doing sports or the school play is a compromise, but really those are options. I had no options in high school. I have always joked I would have rather kissed a girl than wrestled. Sadly, no one wanted to kiss me!

So, this senior is facing the great task of life. Recently, at a workshop, I heard this: "You can get out of school and get a job flipping burgers and make some quick cash and buy a car. That is fine. That is easy. Or, you can sweat and study for another few decades and establish a career as a doctor or professional and buy a car lot. Both choices are fine. In the first case, you went easy first and found life hard. In the second, you went hard first and found life easy. Both choices are fine. You choose."

I prefer learning to aggressively squeeze the finish, lock down positions and dial up the tension before you loosen up. In other words, we teach hard first and easy second.

Deciding what college to attend is like a Las Vegas dessert buffet: you can reach here and there for as much as you want, but just down the way is another exciting treat. Every college is a perfect choice for someone. For me, I wanted to go away to college, yet be in a world-class track program. I turned down schools with academic credentials that still stagger me, but they had lousy track teams.

I managed this compromise well.

Others would have hated Utah State or Harvard or wherever. When we visited Montana for a track meet, I noticed the university cafeteria had wonderful things my Aggie school didn't have. It's a compromise. Yes, you can pick a school by its proximity to a beach or to skiing. You can pick a college by a process only known to you. But, the college ultimately asks you to choose one.

And, that drives seniors crazy. One.

It's not unlike what I told the guy not long ago who wanted to be an O lifter: "You should have been born in Eastern Europe to short, stocky and strong parents."

No, it wasn't great advice, but this is essential in understanding managing compromises: you might not have the opportunity to manage anything because of genetics, environment or the "breaks."

We read about great athletes who throw it away to legal troubles, drugs and other choices. Maybe you could have been the single greatest kayaker of all time, but were born in a desert.

Or, maybe you got hurt on the wrong day and missed the tryout. It happens.

Managing compromises is the greatest challenge we have in life. It's difficult—I would say impossible—to plot an answer. Soon I will have that for you.

Ten Secrets to Building Mass

So you want to put on mass, fast. I have a program that will do just that, but first, some guidelines.

1. Mass building, like fat loss, has to be done at the exclusion of everything else.

A guy with fourteen-inch arms will sometimes ask me about a mass-building program, but worry to death about his six pack (meth addicts have six packs, by the way), his cardio, his game, and about five other things. Once you get sixteen-inch arms, I'll allow you to worry about all those other things.

2. You need to spend time under the bar.

You have to find ways to load and move the weights for up to several minutes without releasing the load by putting the bar down or resting on a machine. This program is based on this insight.

3. You have to eat.

You're now going to stop worrying about every calorie as if you were a college cheerleader. On a mass-gaining program, you must eat. When I put on forty pounds in four months my freshman year in college, I used to eat sandwiches before dinner so I wouldn't be so hungry during dinner. Think *Shark Week* when you sit down to eat and warn the others at the table not to reach across your plate. Likewise, pre-workout nutrition is imperative.

4. You must master resting.

I know there's an urge to do this and that and this after every workout, but for a mass-building program, you have to accept that cardio consists of changing channels with the remote. If you don't sleep eight or more hours every night, it's going to impact your mass gains. Many famous bodybuilders have advocated the muscle nap, a long nap in the afternoon to help gain muscle. Remember, you grow while you rest. Pick-up basketball games are not rest!

5. Bulking programs have very few movements.

Let's put it this way: *good* bulking programs have few movements. When I had my most success with mass building, the number of movements I used was always around seven or eight total. Learn to love them.

6. You need to get some reps in.

Although people have gained amazing mass on lower reps, the load needed to gain mass on a low-rep program is difficult for most people (and mortals). So, until you can handle a 400-pound bench, a 500-pound squat, and a 600-pound deadlift, you're going to need reps to bulk up. There's something magical in mass gains around the five to ten rep range, and the last century of strength enthusiasts will bear this out.

7. Never do fewer than ten reps in the back squat.

There are people who can ignore this advice, powerlifters mainly, but for the bulk of the population this is wise advice. Each and every time you load up the bar on your back, get ten reps in. It gives the needed time under load, and it seems to stimulate the whole body, along with the appetite!

8. Nail your rest periods.

Few beginners know the answer to the question, "How long do you rest between sets?" The correct answer is, "It depends." An advanced lifter might take a year to recover from a record lift, while a new lifter is recharged and ready to go literally seconds after doing a machine movement. For mass building, think around three minutes for the squat and bench, and ninety seconds for the other movements. Your mileage may vary.

9. Leave one or two in the tank.

In non-lifter's terms, always finish a set knowing you could have done a few more reps. We all love the images from *Pumping Iron* with all the forced reps, but for most people who need mass, well, they just aren't there yet. It's better to get an additional set or two than it is to roast on exercise.

10. Pamper yourself (sort of).

This is definitely old-school advice, but "save yourself" on a building program. Wear extra clothes so your body doesn't have to use resources to stay warm. Park closer to the door. Find shorter routes to everything. Sit more. Remember, this isn't a lifetime plan but a short, focused, fiery attempt to gain mass.

The Dan John Bulking Program

This program is based on an older, successful concept of training that repeats the same exercises daily, but each workout is still focused on certain body parts. For example, you'll be focusing on squats on Workout C (lucky you!), but you'll still be repeating the movements from Workouts A and B.

There are several excellent reasons for this.

First, mastery of the movements is a key to mass building. You won't be making great gains if you have to remind yourself to bend your elbows when you bench press; in fact, you may kill yourself.

Second, the best movements for mass building make up a very short list, and you need to do them. A lot. I wish it were more complex than that.

Finally, the best tonic for soreness is to do the movement that got you sore in the first place. Enjoy!

The Exercises

Double Clean and Press

Two dumbbells, one in each hand. Stand tall. Using a bit of a hip hinge, clean the 'bells to shoulder height. From the shoulders, overhead press both to lockout. Return the 'bells to the starting position and re-clean the weight. Press and continue. Each clean and press is one repetition, so a set of ten is ten cleans and presses total.

Back Squat

We'll be doing the back squat each and every workout. There's no more important movement to master in the search for mass.

Straight-Leg Deadlift

This is a "tonic" throughout the program. With soft knees and a light weight, lower the weight down about sock height and stand back up. Try to feel it in the hamstrings, not the lower back.

If you have any issues, don't do this one. It's a post-squat tonic, not a training movement.

Pullup

The pullup serves double duty as a great lat builder and perhaps the best ab exercise I know. I've yet to find someone who can do twenty pullups and can't dominate any test of abdominal strength.

Machine Row

In the past few years, I've changed my tune on machines. The standard barbell bent-over row is marvelous when done correctly. It's that whole issue with "done correctly" that I find issues with. If your facility has a good machine that doesn't stress your lower back, just use it.

Bench Press

With the dumbbell clean and press in the first part of the workout, the bench press will take care of all the other needs for upper body mass and pressing.

Barbell Curls

I hate how the barbell curl is maligned. I've always thought the strict curl is a window into the general strength level of an athlete. I once saw a guy strict curl—no back bend or elbows sliding behind the lats—with 225 pounds. That sight remains burned into my brain. Funny thing, he also had really, really big arms. Go figure.

Farmer Walks

This is my answer to the world's worst strength question, "If all you could do is one movement, what would it be?" If you have the courage to push the weights up to half-bodyweight in each hand and trudge bravely "out there," you'll discover there's not an inch of your body that won't have an opinion about what you did.

Workout A

> *Warmup*
> *Dumbbell clean and press, 3 × 5*
> *Back squat, 3 × 10*
> *Straight-leg deadlift, 1 × 20*
> *Row, 5 × 5*
> *Pullup, 25*
> *Bench press, 3 × 5*
> *Curl, 3 × 5*
> *Farmer walk*

Do one set of the farmer walk with heavy dumbbells. Try to make your walk end in front of the dumbbell racks. You'll thank me later.

Workout B

> *Warmup*
> *Dumbbell clean and press, 5 × 5*
> *Back squat, 2 × 10*
> *Straight-leg deadlift, 1 × 20*
> *Row, 3 × 5*
> *Pullup, 15*
> *Bench press, 5 × 5*
> *Curl, 3 × 10*
> *Farmer walk, 2*

Do two sets of the walks today. Walk out as far as you can from the rack and put the weights down. Then…return them.

Workout C

> *Warmup*
> *Dumbbell clean and press, 3 × 5*
> *Back squat, 5 × 10*
> *Straight-leg deadlift, 1 × 20*
> *Row, 2 × 5*
> *Pullup, 12*
> *Bench press, 3 × 5*
> *Curl, 2 × 5 plus 1 × 10*
> *Farmer walk, 2*

Strive for a heavier 'bell in the walks each week. Make yourself push this to the limit. Walk a long way, stop, refresh, and try to go a little farther. I always had a target or goal to get to. Remember that you have to come back, too.

After six weeks of these workouts and lots of food, assess your progress. I like to begin the program with a "before" picture and finish it with an "after" picture. Bodyweight gains depend on a lot of factors, but I've seen these common-sense programs and approaches do far better than some of the voodoo we often see on the web.

The Four Pillars of Strength Training

THERE WAS A POINT WHEN it became obvious my wife and I were going to have to spend a lot of money.

When we bought our house, one of the selling points was a magnificent deck overlooking the Jordan River. (Not the one in the Bible, and, no, I can't walk on water. Yet.) Through that deck's years, I've stained, painted, sanded, stripped, sawed and replaced enough wood to sail away on a boat.

Then, on a bright blue, snow-packed day, we noticed an issue. The pillars were rotting. I kicked one and the pillar just evaporated. Unless I'm the *Six Million Dollar Man* or a slightly less chartreuse Hulk, this was going to be a problem.

Obviously, we needed a new deck.

That deck is a metaphor for all of us in this game of strength and conditioning. We spend a lot of time preparing our bodies for whatever goals we've outlined, yet if the pillars are rotting, the whole thing is liable to tumble down with one kick.

I offer the following four pillars of strength training as a means to forestall the effects of bad programming, bad exercise selection and bad ideas so you can build a strong, functional and presumably esthetic body, along with enjoying a long, healthy career.

Pillar One: Time

It's going to take some time to get your goals. Recently, Stephanie Brown Trafton, the 2008 Gold Medal winner at the Olympics in the discus, stated this:

> *"Fine-tuning the discus will take several years. You have to really develop a base for it, and then, after about ten years of throwing, you get to the point where you're really solid in the technique that you have and you just need to have your little tweaking here and there."*

That insight alone will make most of us cry: after ten years of training, you can go ahead and tweak things a little.

Contrast that with all the hype we read in most training advertisements. In fact, tally up the number of things you've purchased through the years promising this or that "in as little as two weeks."

I've said the following about 10,000 times: Everything works… for about six weeks. In ten years, that's a lot of "six weeks."

That's the reason I recommend adding things to your training program every so often just to shake things up a little. Taking a minute to do a single dip or chinup is well worth the effort even if it's just to discover how much intensity it takes to move a load at that rate of speed.

Bored with your training? Dust off Tom Platz's old squat workouts. They're simple and fun. One day a week, go really heavy on the back squat. The other day, take a weight like 225 and do as many reps as you can. My best in the deep Olympic style back squat with 225 pounds is fifty-one reps. I've heard, and this is not unlike "someone's brother's friend's uncle," the record is 100 reps. Go ahead, beat it.

If you're thinking you have time to get your goals, you can experiment with things that a narrow focus won't allow you to do. In my personal history book called My Training Journals, you'll find Nautilus training, bodybuilding, powerlifting, preseason prep for flag football, high-rep squats, CrossFit, triathlon training and a host of other less popular ideas right alongside my training for the Olympic lifts and the discus.

Pillar Two: Harvest Layoffs

You'll notice that I didn't say "take" layoffs. Enjoy them. And here I'm not talking about skipping a workout or two, or missing a week for a vacation or a business trip. I'm talking about taking up to six weeks of doing nothing.

Remember, if you believe in the first pillar, this ties right in.

This isn't a new idea, either. Not long ago, nutritional expert Lyle McDonald loaned me a book called *Physiology of Strength,* by Theodor Hettinger. Now, this book was published in 1961, yet everything we know about strength is in there, and like I often say about John McCallum, the rest of us are footnotes.

Some of my favorite insights from the book include:

- The calves can increase in strength six percent a week, the glutes four percent, the triceps three percent, and the biceps two percent. When I fall back into my hunter paradigm for understanding why humans react to training, it shouldn't be a surprise to see the sprinting muscles respond to training very quickly.

- Men are stronger than women. In tests, some parts of women are fifty-five percent as strong as men (forearm extensors), but in the hip area it rises to eighty percent. Anyone who's ever coached women will find that research to be absolutely true. Women tend to have the odd ability to bench 135 for ten reps, yet their max will be 140 for a single.

- Strength peaks in the late twenties, maintains for a long time, and then gradually declines, especially in untrained populations. Oh, that is sadly true.

- It's easier to train in the summer, and vitamin D might help that, too. No surprise here, but it's amazing to see the graph that shows why January training is so lousy. I thought it was just the snow.

- Injecting testosterone seemed to make everybody train better for a long time. Welcome to the modern world of sport.

One of the areas that really interested me in Hettinger's book was the discussion on layoffs. It's important to remember the period this book was written, as the short (and woefully inaccurate) retelling of the following story probably couldn't happen in today's university setting.

In an interesting 200-day study, Hettinger tested the normal strength levels of several people. One arm on each of several subjects was put in a plaster cast for seven days. (I'm sure they used the Soviet method of volunteering: You!) After seven days in a cast, it took a short amount of time to get back to normal.

From there, they continued to train the people up to a level where the volunteers were thirty-percent stronger than the starting "normal" strength level. Then, the arms were put back in the casts. Strength levels dropped, but not back to the starting level.

The interesting thing was this: it took only about half the time to return to that level of thirty-percent stronger when the cast was removed.

Those of us who've trained a while, of course, aren't surprised. I've heard it called "muscle memory," among other things, but I think it's true in all areas of the game.

For those interested in absolute fat loss, John McCallum, of *Keys to Progress* fame, had an idea called "softening up" for fat loss. I know plenty of people argue that one needs to constantly be in a state of three-percent bodyfat, but very few people have ever done it. McCallum's idea was to stagger highly focused fat-loss training (zero carbs, full body workouts and some easy jogging) with a period of general training and a laxer diet.

It's the layoff that propels the next round of intensive training. Anyone reading this who's tried to lose fat by increasingly rigorous diet plans and exercise schemes usually finds they hit a brick wall.

I have an old friend from my days studying at an intensive foreign language institute who struggled through the last week of prep for a bodybuilding contest, then walked into a pizza parlor and ate three pizzas. That meal had an effect on his body, if you're looking for an understatement. His fogged-out brain just demanded mounds of carbs and salt.

I'm not sure if an earlier layoff would have helped, but he later told me he tried to be perfect for three months, and he only had that one lapse, which sadly happened just hours before prejudging. For some, that would actually help them look better on stage, but once he fell off the wagon, he didn't stop rolling down the hill.

This is also the reason I push for high school and adolescent athletes to do multiple sports. Those "layoffs" from one set of movements to another—one season to another—allow the athlete to rebuild and avoid overuse injuries. I'm convinced the plague of ACL injuries in high school female athletes is caused by the club sport system.

Of course, those club coaches get paid by having a lot of kids in the sport year round, and I get paid one step from nothing as a coach, so what do I know?

Don't be afraid to take time off now and then. You'll quickly return to your normal strength levels and find a new discipline to deal with severe dieting. It also provides a chance to look around and explore some other avenues for your strength and health goals.

Pillar Three: You Have to Move Heavy Weights

The problem with all the options in a modern gym, besides being too many, is the fact that we have no honest system for measuring the amount of weight used. With the cams, the counterweights and the plate-stacking systems, it's all too easy to trick ourselves into thinking we're really moving iron.

I'm not trying to brag here, but I went with my wife and daughter to a local gym and moved from machine to machine, stacking the weights for safe, controlled reps. The max effort I could do at this place is really not much of an effort for any typical high school athlete.

So, you have to lift heavy.

Not long ago, Doug Dunagan talked with Brian Oldfield about his training. Brian is a legend in the strength sports—he's the first man to throw the shot seventy-five feet. Go ahead, pick up something sixteen pounds and throw it. If you measure half of Brian's effort, you're probably in the one-percent club.

Doug described Brian's lifting like this:

> *"His lifting was done on Mondays and Thursdays, and he generally worked with five sets of doubles. On the push press and front squat, he did triples. Sometimes he did ten sets because often he felt that his fifth set was the easiest."*

> *Bench, 5 × 2, 401*
> *Clean and press, 5 × 2, 364*
> *Snatch (split and squat), 5 × 2, 250*
> *Front squat, 5 × 3, 465 (500 single)*
> *Push press/jerk, 5 × 3, 365–450*

Brian had a little formula that still makes sense. To add a foot to one's effort in the shot put, he needs to add fifteen pounds to the max on each lift. Brian's workout was the same for this period: Tuesday and Thursday he'd repeat all five lifts.

Recently, Brian told me a little gem about counting reps for an explosive athlete. On a trip to Poland, he went to a local school where the kids were in a physical education class. They weren't just playing dodgeball, that's for sure. Brian was watching the kids doing overhead squats. They were counting for each other: *10-9-8-7-6-5-4-3-2-1.*

He had the idea that for explosive athletes that NASA countdown method reflected the real way we view lifting: it's the launch pad to take off! It's a small change, but try it. It really does work.

Vince Gironda said it best years ago: "It's not high reps that work. It's not heavy weights that work. It's high reps with heavy weights that work!"

Pillar Four: There's a Time and Place for Hypertrophy

It's odd to even have to discuss this in bodybuilding circles, but many people have extreme views on hypertrophy training, and it usually ends in "never" or "always." The answer is actually a bit more like an "S" that's fallen drunk on its side.

In my perfect world, the beginning bodybuilder would spend some quality time learning the basics:

- Start with the row, squat, pullup, bench press, biceps curl and an intelligent abdominal move. (Right, Arnold's "big six.")

- Understand the need for protein, fish oil and fiber and eating meals that don't have a clown selling them.

- Enjoy a basic understanding of the body and how the body moves.

- Embrace the notion that pain is part of the path.

Now, we can add some mass.

Do it the right way by slowly ramping up the weights and adding reps to nearly every workout for a while.

Variation will have its place, but like we always say, "Same, but different." Some variation in the basic moves is one thing; 1,001 variations is another.

Hypertrophy's first phase should last until the gains begin to slow. Hopefully, this stage of the career will parallel the athlete's attempts in team or Olympic sports.

I've come to describe building muscle as "armor building" for the sport athlete. There's a need for some mass and the protection that mass delivers for the contact athlete.

On a side note, I once had a guy tell me that "armor building" was a bad term, as "any excess hypertrophy would lead to diminished skills in other qualities of the athlete."

My eyes might be getting bad, but it was obvious to me from this gentleman's build that he'd never been blindsided on a kick-off. If you missed the point, when someone is trying to take your head off, a little mass might be the difference between a headache and a headstone.

After a period of time, though, it's time to rethink pure hypertrophy training.

At the next stage, the gentle downward slope after the initial year(s) of easy muscle gain, I always argue to put pure hypertrophy on the shelf, and then play around with some other things. Watching strongman contests on television will give you the insight that maybe doing farmer walks or pulling massively heavily objects for distance might help your body gain some mass.

On another tack, it might also be a time to look at a dedicated leaning-out phase. I noted earlier that a serious fat-loss attack seems to lead to greater muscle mass when you go back to normal eating and training. If you're continuing an athletic career, there may be no better advice than to expand into strongman training and look at some fat loss. If the recent track and field Nationals taught me one thing, it's this: Elite athletes ain't fat.

What most people don't realize is what happens in the next stage. As we age, the need for hypertrophy training increases compared to other training qualities. The master athlete might need to focus on maintaining or increasing muscle mass.

Let this be said: It's assumed the older athlete has the necessary techniques and a base in some kind of strength training. As we age into our middle years and beyond, winning the fight to hold muscle mass is probably the single best indicator of health.

As we prepare to enter Sunnybrook Senior Center, the bulk of our training probably shouldn't be shuffleboard. Rather, we should be doing a program with roots in training for Mr. America. Bodypart training, split routines, machine training, high-rep work, isolated muscle training and a rigid adherence to sets, reps and rest periods is the appropriate protocol.

The hypertrophy curve is based on reality. All too often we ignore that first dip and keep striving for more and more.

Give yourself four or five years of armor building, then move into some other areas of strength training. For the athlete, certainly make sure you're training for hypertrophy some of the time, but never fully drop those higher-rep workouts from the training program. Leave room for the Olympic and power lifts, but don't abandon the mass work.

Build It Right, Build It Forever

That new deck was finished at a cost higher than what most of us make in a year. According to the builder, no one will ever have to mess with it in my lifetime (he knows my age).

If you build the proper foundation, you won't have to mess around, either.

Armor Building

THERE ARE MANY REASONS WHY most people don't achieve their physical goals. I've come to the conclusion that the number one reason is trying to do everything all the time.

I'll get a question about mass building and will recommend lots of squats, lots of food and lots of rest. The follow-up question from the same person will usually include something about "six-pack abs," agility work and dunking a basketball.

This is too much!

Much of the confusion stems from the fact that I basically use one tool—the barbell—and its close cousins like kettlebells, dumbbells and the like, to help folks accomplish their goals, from fat loss and muscle gain to mobility and flexibility.

Most people need to find periods in the year, usually from three to six weeks, perhaps as long as eight weeks, to work hard on specific qualities.

For example, the Velocity Diet is amazing for fat loss, but it would be hard to do while also in an NFL training camp. It doesn't mean the Velocity Diet is bad, nor does it mean training camp is right or wrong. This isn't moral theology. Yet this is precisely the kind of thought process that destroys most people's training plans.

Trying to Do (or Be) Everything All the Time

There are times to burn fat, build muscle, get more explosive or prep for a sport, but it's nearly impossible to do this all the time. And there are some qualities you should only work at for a little while and only when you need it.

I work with a lot of people from collision sports and collision occupations. One of the hardest things to do while preparing for these endeavors is what I call "armor building," a term one of my football players coined a few years ago.

At first I didn't understand what he meant. Basically, he felt that some of the exercises we were doing, in his case the thick barbell curl and the double-kettlebell front squat, were helping him be a better running back. It gave him a feeling "like armor."

A few years ago, I worked with a high school running back, Tony, who had a coach who didn't believe in weightlifting. (The coach probably also didn't like these new-fangled automobiles, either.)

After a few sessions of working with him, he found that doing what he called "The Exercise"—a combination of power snatches and overhead squats—gave him some tools no one else on the field had. In his last five football games his senior year, Tony ran for over 200 yards each game.

Callusing

The great fighter Ken Shamrock calls this callusing—a focused attempt to prepare an athlete for contact. When I wrestled in high school, I would spend the first week or so stuffing wet toilet paper up my nose, as it bled every session. Magically, around week two, that very same forearm to the face wouldn't cause a drop of blood to come out.

While there will definitely be some callusing, the armor-building training will also include specific movements to gear up for collisions. Strangely, most of the athletes I have do this program note that they also look better in the mirror. In a sense, armor building is a kind of bodybuilding for sport.

The most basic moves might also be the most exhausting. Every football player should have some intense loathing for grass drills, which are also known as "Up-Downs." The coach has a whistle, and the job is to run in place driving the knees high. When Coach blows the whistle, you throw yourself to the ground and leap back up to running in place. The running in place, as you soon discover, is the easy part.

Grass drills alone can prepare us for many things. Late in my high school football career, I realized that of all the things we did for conditioning, most had no carryover to the games. But as much as I hated them, grass drills seemed to be the most "game-like."

Football, rugby and war are much about getting on the ground as fast as you can and then getting back up. I remember one of my teammates complaining about practice, especially up-downs. He was a star in middle school and was learning that getting to puberty first was great, but you had to keep working afterwards. I noticed that all the guys who never played felt that the hard work was a waste of time.

I'll Tumble for Ya

If you don't have access to a high school football coach with a whistle, try just some rolling. I'm a firm believer that tumbling and rolling is the missing link in most people's training.

Tim Anderson has been writing a lot about how rolling "resets" the body. I know one of the great fears of adulthood is to say, and here comes the advertisement, "I've fallen and I can't get up." I'm proactive about almost everything and would rather practice falling and getting up.

My standard "do this" tumbling training is this:

- *5 Somersaults (forward rolls)*
- *5 Right shoulder rolls*
- *5 Left shoulder rolls*
- *4 Ninja rolls (right shoulder roll, left shoulder roll, right, left)*
- *Bear crawl*
- *3 Cartwheels facing one direction*
- *3 Cartwheels facing the other*

And finally, as I always joke, run to the bucket.

For whatever reason, tumbling seems to affect the tummy at first. You can think of it as a lousy but effective diet program.

For many, grass drills and tumbling tossed into some training weeks once or twice a year is a fun jumpstart to a fat-loss program, or even just a nice way to keep the motor running toward the end of a serious ripping program.

One reason I like the Turkish getup so much is that it's a kind of Tai Chi grass drill or tumbling session. Conversely, I rarely see the typical fitness enthusiast touch the ground, save for planks, and that's an exercise that wavers in popularity.

Remember the axiom: "If no one in a typical gym is doing something, it's probably pretty hard to do." Rolling around on the floor doing getups is an insightful, thoughtful way to get reacquainted with getting off the ground.

And as you age, learning to catch a fall, recover and get up might be the secret to a more vigorous old age. Trust me: you will get older nearly every year.

Barbell Armor

With the barbell, there are several great armor-building moves. As noted, the thick barbell curl has been one of my odder go-to movements for a few years. I'm not sure what it does to the forearms, elbows and guns, but try them. I use both actual fat bars and those new grips that mimic the metal. Your budget will decide which way you go on this.

Thick bars are expensive, but the curl and deadlift movements are stunning to do with them. The thick bar curl can be done for reps up to ten, but I fail when the reps go up. For whatever reason, this exercise seems to get the body ready to take a hit.

The snatch-grip deadlift and the duck-foot deadlift (heels together, toes out) also seem to help the collision athlete. This compromised position tends to wake up more of the system, especially the connective tissue. I've gone heavy with snatch-grip deadlifts in my career, and I always seemed to be able to take a whack or two.

Correlation or causation is never too important to me because these two movements are quickly taxing, and we won't need a deep philosophy discussion after doing them.

For squatting, I hate the Zercher squat. Hate it. It kills me, but I've always noticed my human inner tube seems much more powerful after doing these. This is that odd internal pressure—talk to a martial arts person for more details about internal pressure.

Also, holding the bar in the crook of the elbow is callusing for the ages. I've also experienced, as many brighter people than me have, that the Zercher squat demands a kind of moving mobility that has to be experienced to understand. If you hate Zerchers, you're probably doing them right.

With kettlebells, I have a "funny" challenge for you:

- 1 double-kettlebell clean and 1 double-kettlebell front squat
- 2 double-kettlebell cleans and 2 double-kettlebell front squats
- 3 double-kettlebell cleans…and you see where this is heading

Here's the challenge: go all the way up to ten and ten with the twenty-four-kilo 'bells (thirty-twos if you're really serious) without putting them down.

So far, no takers!

To recap:

- Grass drills
- Tumbling
- Getups
- Thick barbell curls
- Duck-stance deadlifts
- Snatch-grip deadlifts
- Zercher squats
- Double- kettlebell cleans and front squats

Beware: each of these has the ability to bring forth an odd kind of soreness.

You can do armor building for about three weeks. Reps and sets must be open ended. Without a coach blowing a whistle at you, it's going to be tough to push through some of these.

Week One

Generally, week one should emphasize getups and some tumbling. In the weightroom, try a few simple moves. You should be fine tuning your conditioning and basic technical skills too. Try to spend the bulk of your time prepping for the season.

Monday

> *General warmup*
> *Getups*
> *General orientation into the tumbling moves*
> *(practice!)*
> *Double-kettlebell cleans and front squats*
> *(practice!)*

Tuesday

> *General warmup*
> *Snatch-grip deadlifts*
> *Zercher squat*
> *Thick barbell curls*

Wednesday

> *General warmup*
> *Getups*
> *General orientation into the tumbling*
> *moves. Try doing a basic rolling sequence.*
> *Double-kettlebell cleans and front squats.*
> *Try getting to 5 + 5.*

Thursday

Sports practice only

Friday

General warmup
Getups
General orientation into the tumbling
   moves. Try doing a basic rolling sequence.
Double-kettlebell cleans and front squats.
   Strive for two sets of 5 + 5.

Saturday

General warmup
Duck-stance deadlifts
Snatch-grip deadlifts
Thick barbell curls

Week Two

Monday

General warmup
Getups
Duck-stance deadlifts
Snatch-grip deadlifts
Zercher squats
Thick barbell curls

Tuesday

General warmup
Tumbling

> Double-kettlebell cleans and front squats
>   *(Try to get beyond 5 + 5)*
> Grass drills

Wednesday and Friday

Repeat Monday

Saturday

Repeat Tuesday

Week Three

Monday

> General warmup
> Tumbling
> Double-kettlebell cleans and front squats
> Grass drills

Tuesday

> General warmup
> Getups
> Duck-stance deadlifts
> Snatch-grip deadlifts
> Zercher squats
> Thick barbell curls

Wednesday and Friday

Repeat Monday

Saturday

Repeat Tuesday

You may ask where your beloved bench press is on this program, or whatever your heart desires that's missing. Well, add it in! Or as I usually suggest, leave it out. It's only three weeks and we're trying to use our valuable time to literally toughen the skin and body for contact.

Even if you're not a collision athlete, there's still a lot of value in trying some of these lifts and moves. From a fat-burning perspective, you're going to have a hard time finding movements more compelling than grass drills and tumbling. With the odd barbell moves, you're going to discover the beautiful simplicity of the basic deadlift and squat when you return to them.

So here's the lesson: when it's time to kick it up a notch, you need to take a few weeks aside and really attack it.

If you need to get some calluses and build some armor, take some time to do it before you need it.

Maximal Fat Loss, Minimal Equipment

THERE'S A FUNNY THING you start to notice about exercise and fat loss: the better you get at the movement, the less effective the exercise becomes for burning fat. We see this odd phenomenon in every discipline, from performance to group aerobics—people slowly getting chubbier and chubbier as they continue to train.

It comes down to efficiency, or lack of it. You see, fat-loss exercise has to be inefficient.

There's a simple way to rediscover the joys and sorrows of inefficiency, and it's literally at your feet: the ground. If you get on the ground and then get off the ground, you'll stimulate a lot of fat loss. It's really quite surprising. As such, I present the following fat-loss combos, each designed around kissing the good Earth.

Grounded to the Ground

When I evaluate training programs, typically two big omissions stare at me:

1. The lack of appropriate squatting movements.
2. The lack of loaded carries (just doing a farmer walk is enough).

The third area involves the kind of groundwork people are doing. Case in point: if Phil Maffetone is correct and 28,000 Americans a year die from falls or fall-related injuries, we should stop being so paranoid about peanut butter and focus more on tumbling.

Better still, groundwork training has minimal equipment needs. Let's explore some basics.

Here's a great workout. Stand up. Now, get to the ground and lie on your back. Repeat this for five minutes. Back in the day these were called grass drills, or up-downs, or "fun time," depending on the school. My football coaches always told me that getting off the ground after being knocked down was the secret to success in football. Frankly, it works for life, too.

I did a program from Pat Flynn where each session begins with five minutes of naked Turkish getups, which is just a formalized version of the grass drill. You can do them naked if you like, but in this case, the term "naked" means doing them without any resistance. Oddly enough, every day I find I move and feel better after the groundwork.

To really turn groundwork into something special, though, we need to combine it with other fat-burning modalities. For instance, if you followed the 10,000 Swing Challenge, you know all about one of the great furnace movements, the swing. Combining them with the pushup (or the plank, if you have issues) works great.

Here are my favorite combos. Be sure to just pick one for each training day:

Combo Option One

> *Swings × 20 seconds*
> *Pushups × 6*
> *Rest × 30 seconds*

Repeat for 15 minutes

Next workout, increase the pushups by one.

Combo Option Two

At the top of the minute:
Swings × 20, pushups × 10
Rest the remainder of the minute.
Swings × 20, pushups × 9
Rest the remainder of the minute.

Continue until you hit swings × 20,
pushup × 1

This will take 10 minutes. To increase the workout to 15 minutes, start with swings × 20, pushups × 15 instead of 10.

The next workout, do 21 swings each minute.

Combo Option Three

This option differs from Option Two in that you don't take any rest.

Swings × 20
Pushups × 10

Keep the swings × 20 and...

Work down the pushups: 9, 8, 7, 6, 5, 4, 3, 2, 1

Combo Option Four

Swings × 10, goblet squats × 10, pushups × 10
Swings × 10, goblet squats × 9, pushups × 9

Continue until you hit:

Swings × 10, goblet squats × 1, pushups × 1

No rest!

Combo Option Five

On the minute:

Swings × 1 and pushup × 1

Then farmer walk the weight to the top of the next minute

Swings × 2 and pushup × 2

Then farmer walk the weight to the top of the next minute

Continue until you're finished.

The Skinny

What you'll quickly discover is that getting up and getting down, over and over, adds a metabolic hit that you won't expect. For a complete program, mix planks or pushups with sprints of various distances. This has to be done in an area with a fair amount of space, but both the pushup numbers and the sprint quality will degrade quickly.

We recently began exploring a new combination with one of my NFL clients. Equipment issues are minimal—these are like the Litvinovs I discussed years ago.

It's a deadlift for five reps followed by a bear crawl. Everyone seems to be doing monkey aerobics and caveman cardio, and the bear crawl is getting a bit overdone, but try this very simple combo.

I suggest underloading the deadlift the first workout—back off to about two-thirds of what you think your five-rep max weight would be. Do it for a few sets before worrying about the load. For the bear crawls, make it twenty meters. Since the deadlift load is relatively light, do more sets, up to eight total.

Not only do the heart and lungs take a hit, but this combination leads to an odd kind of soreness that really has to be tasted to be understood.

Inefficiency

Fat loss demands inefficiency. For a fat-burning program that's hyper-efficient and short on equipment needs, try doing two days of the swing and pushup combos. Keep these at least two days apart from each other.

One day a week, get out and mix the pushup and plank with sprints. Copy the old running tradition of fartlek, which means "speed play." Start off with just one or two pushups followed by an easy jog or even a walk.

Mix and match the length of runs and the intensity (the speed) of the running with the number of pushups. Make it chaotic and just play with the two exercises.

Finally, one other day of the week try the deadlift and bear crawl combination. Work up to eight sets of five in the deadlift.

On to the Next One

None of these workouts last very long—rarely over fifteen minutes—but you'll never fully master them.

Let the ground be part of your fat-loss program.

Band of Meatheads—
The Glories of Group Training

I HAVE THIS ODD RELATIONSHIP with the local blue jays.

Every night, before I go to bed, I put out some peanuts. In the morning, I wake up to jays squawking and barking while they hop and pop on my balcony. This noise wakes me up and I start my day.

Now you can argue that I should invest in an alarm clock, and honestly, I use one if I have to get to the airport by five. But on most days, my feathered friends wake me up pretty much at the same time. Of course, if I don't put out peanuts I get up earlier, as they object mightily to my oversight.

Like the jays, I believe in community. I believe it so much that I'm going to leap into the key point: You'll never make your long-term goals in fitness without community.

Now before I go too far, you can see where a seemingly contradictory idea might be heading: You can't make your goals unless you have the courage to train alone. But that concept is for another time.

Since all of us need to spend a little time on both sides, let's take a look at the difference a community makes.

251

The Three Ps

There are three Ps in training in groups, and each is important, so important that you may gloss over them and ignore the fundamental importance of the concepts of path, passion and program.

Let's look at each.

The Path

Although I don't use it professionally, I have a master's degree in history. It really does come in handy in my social life, even though I don't make money from it.

You see, as you age, you tend to become fascinated by certain odd things. I have a friend who reads everything he can find on Custer's Last Stand, so much so that he has a list of names of his friends whose last names are somehow mentioned in the musters of the battle. I can't imagine anything sexier than meeting a woman at a party and telling her that someone with her family name died at Little Big Horn.

What happens is that people will begin to talk about their interest in Little Big Horn or D-Day or the Battle of Hastings or whatever, and I follow along well. But when the Little Big Horn guy talks to the guy who's fascinated by the assassination of JFK, they have a disconnect.

As my professors taught me, I'll teach you: They don't understand the connections; they don't see the links.

How will this concept help you? Well, we're still in a time where people think that one kind of training is "right" and another is "wrong." That's moral theology (and, sadly, I'm your guy for this, too).

Even "better" or "worse" doesn't help much here. We're in a time where you can get into an internet war by telling people you tried an abdominal exercise or you did five sets of four rather than five sets of five.

That's not community; that's a pissing match.

One of the great things about going to gyms, attending workshops or competing in a strength contest is that you'll get exposed to the path. One of the reasons I'm confident in discussing weight training is that I had a long, fun career as an Olympic lifter. I've lifted in a powerlifting meet, taken my place in a Strongman comp, tossed a few cabers and allowed my abs to be seen on computer screens all over the world.

The path is an interesting training tool. As I tell people at every workshop, "Success leaves tracks." Why not save yourself a lot of time, effort and even stupidity by asking someone who's been there before?

Honestly, if you want fat loss, ask a bodybuilder.

I recently sat down with Josh Hillis and in five minutes, he shared the "secrets" of fat loss.

I'll share just one: You need a food log.

According to Josh, literally every approach to fat loss works as long as you stick to it. Rather than ten minutes on a treadmill to soak his clients for more money, you'll find Josh going over their weekly logs. If the logs aren't filled in, Josh's clients don't do anything until they are.

I became a better coach by asking Josh that question, and then we went on to detail this in our book *Fat Loss Happens on Monday*.

If you want to bulk quickly, ask the people who've bulked up quickly—people like me.

It involves high-rep squats and lots of complexes. And no, you can't do those workouts very often. How do I know this? I've walked that path. I've made a lot of mistakes, and now I can teach you how to follow the right route.

Don't try to invent a hodgepodge program of "a little this and a little that" with an emphasis on the latter. Follow the best.

And how do you get all of that great information? Ask!

The Passion

The next key for understanding the role of community in fitness training is passion.

The roots of passion are in a Latin word meaning "to suffer." I love training. I really do. And, because of my great love for training, I also enjoy the suffering. As I recount the scars, the surgeries and the battles of my athletic career, I feel the surge of the rising heartbeat and my hair standing on end. Like Patton said, "By God, I love it."

Yet, it's hard to get that fired up about three sets of eight with a medium weight on a military press machine. So, to fire your passion, meet with a group of buddies and train.

I've had the rare opportunity of having Mark Twight bring over the elite of the elite to train with me in my backyard. True, they have a skill set in some things that stagger me, but lifting weights and pulling sleds staggers them.

So, while the meat is on the grill, we sweat, strain and vomit.

At another point in time, I'd regularly meet a group of mostly middle-aged (I'm being polite) people with a love of conditioning. My friend Dan Martin calls this concept "virtual stone soup." I realize now that most people don't know this fine story, so here's a bland example.

> *"Some travelers come to a village, carrying nothing more than an empty pot. Upon their arrival, the villagers are unwilling to share any of their food with the hungry travelers. The travelers fill the pot with water,*

drop a large stone in it, and place it over a fire in the village square. One of the villagers becomes curious and asks what they're doing. The travelers answer that they're making 'stone soup,' which tastes 'wonderful,' although it still needs a little bit of garnish, which they're missing, to improve the flavor.

"The villager doesn't mind parting with just a little bit of carrot to help them out, so it gets added to the soup. Another villager walks by, inquiring about the pot, and the travelers again mention their stone soup hasn't reached its full potential yet. The villager hands them a little bit of seasoning to help them out. More and more villagers walk by, each adding another ingredient. Finally, a delicious and nourishing pot of soup is enjoyed by all."

Our communal training sessions were of this variety. We all brought tools, from equipment to life experiences to sandwiches. We'd gather and train, work on issues, and improve a little. We fell in love again with movement and muscle.

When we train in groups, we reignite our passion for all of this.

I've been training groups for so long that sometimes I ignore basic principles I learned the hard way. One of the keys to working in a group, especially in something physical, is to understand that you—and perhaps this is even literally true—become part of an organism.

A group becomes a living being.

You may have found yourself running "gassers" or "finishers" in a sport and realized there's no way you'd ever put yourself through that lung-bursting crap again. But, with a team of like-minded lunatics, off you go again at the sound of the whistle. It's underappreciated, and one of the secrets of really moving up to the next level.

Something as simple as having a training partner waiting for you at the gym will pull you up and get you out the door. If you know a dozen people are eager to work with you, you'll probably get there early.

That's why group training has such a big impact on our long-term success—we do things we might not normally do even with the best intentions. And we humans have this odd ability to handle more suffering if we do it in a group.

Moreover, it's also more fun. I've had people vomit on my shoes and say thank you for the opportunity to do the work.

The Programming

Everyone seems to be an expert at programming now. I've decided I'm clueless about it, as I get email almost daily asking me for a program to do this or that or this. I can't seem to help anyone in this area for a number of good reasons.

First, I don't know the first thing about you or your situation. Second, when I say do X and you do Y, thinking Y is X, I'm so lost in the algebra that I can't catch up to you.

That's why I love programming with a group.

First, no one asks what I think is the most idiotic and impossible-to-answer question, "How much rest time between sets?" The answer is somewhere between seconds and years.

There's an excellent training tactic from Steve Ilg where he has the athlete keep contact with the barbell or dumbbell during rest periods. Yes, simply keep touching the 'bell. It's a dynamic change of mindset to not lose contact with the tool. In group work, rest periods tend to last as long as it takes someone else to finish.

If you're going to have twenty-minute rest periods, this might not be your technique.

Second, and this might seem odd, but the program changes because of the suggestions of the group membership.

If someone needs work on a movement or a body issue, that "Hey, can we do some deadlifts?" becomes a game changer. If you keep the number of people from five to twelve, you'll find that most of the plans coming into the workout change completely as people ask to work on specific issues. Not surprisingly, most of us need the same work, too.

Most of us know the great group programs, or at least you should know them:

I Go/You Go

If there's nearly a perfect program, I'd put "I go/you go" in the conversation. Not only does it restrict and focus rest periods, it keeps everyone engaged by assisting a partner at some level. Need more rest? Then try "I go/you go/they go" by adding a third partner.

The Chain and the Staggered Chain

The chain has multiple meanings, but I've always been a fan of using the term to describe the kind of workout where you start with one dumbbell, move it a few times, and then move to the next dumbbell, repeating the movement up the rack (and back down, if you wish). This workout is also called "the rack" and "up and downs," as you can probably imagine.

Follow the Leader

Boy, has this gem been lost the past few decades. This was a standard way to train when I was coming up, and it's basically vanished. I do a movement for a certain number of reps, the next guy steps up and matches it, and then we move to something else. Just follow the person ahead of you and keep up.

In the old Universal Gyms, this method could accommodate up to thirty people with the instruction of "just do what the guy ahead of you is doing." It's a full-body workout that's easy to follow and easy to keep organized.

A Group at Work

Let's look at an actual workout based on these principles. Our old Coyote Point group used all of these principles.

First, we had two rules: Don't get hurt. Okay, here comes an old beat-up joke, but pay attention. The overriding rule here is not to get hurt. The joke is simple: You ask what the second rule is and I say, "Don't get hurt." There's your ab workout as you laugh hysterically for several minutes. Or not.

Second, part of the workout is driving to the park, unloading the equipment, catching up on the lives of the others and talking about what we were going to eat later.

And lastly, strive to do every human movement in training. This is a principle I've based my career on.

To warm up, do a variety of walks and carries with reasonable kettlebells and a series of basic lifts, stretches and mobility work, nothing too serious.

One thing I sometimes add is a small version of Litvinovs as part of the warmup—see the original *Never Let Go* book for details. After either an easy set of swings or goblet squats, take a stride—a medium-speed, sprint-like run for forty meters or so. The goal is to get four to eight of these as a platform for the later work.

I Go/You Go in a Group

This ratio of work, literally one to one but still with the group, is a valuable hypertrophy-training trick. You have just enough rest to catch your breath before you're back at it. Don't go heavy here, but for movements that'll give you a pump, this is ideal. I love these for basic bodybuilding moves, but they also work for harder things like squat variations and some presses.

Staggered Chain

In a perfect world, you could train like I train people. We randomly, without any concern for weight, toss our kettlebells into a long line on the ground (you can do this with dumbbells too). Then, starting with the left hand, do an exercise like a clean and press, and walk down the line of kettlebells switching hands each time. Next time, start with your right hand. As long as you do an even number of times through, you'll balance out both sides.

Recently, we laid out fifteen kettlebells in a row and each did three times for two loops. The number of presses in five minutes was ninety reps. This is the way to do volume work!

Follow the Leader

If you're in a gym, you have an ideal way of group training, and you don't even know it. You can also do this without a group by training on any piece of recently vacated equipment.

Not long ago, we did this variation with a group of twenty people at my old facility:

Farmer walk
Sled pull
Judy carry (Judy is a 150-pound bag named
after someone I didn't care for very much)
Kettlebell swings
Military presses
Easy run (to a playground)
Pullups (on a jungle gym)
Easy run
Judy carry
Sled pull
Farmer walk

By the time I finished, some of the group was just beginning. Everyone seemed to follow the person in front of them perfectly, and there was virtually zero instruction. When the last person finished, most of the equipment was already put away and the meat was on the grill.

What Those Little Birdies Taught Me

There's a great lesson in my odd relationship with the blue jays, the peanuts and waking up: We all seem to get what we want with less effort than going at it alone. Use the same concept to propel yourself to your goals.

The Tabata Method, Perfected

IN THE BOOK *The Way of the Peaceful Warrior,* there's a great part where Dan Millman is standing on a bridge. "I wonder how deep the water is?" he wonders aloud. His mentor, Socrates, picks him up and throws him into the water. Millman no longer has to wonder.

If I could make most people stop doing one thing, it would be wondering. This is especially true when it comes to the Tabata method, an interval training concept I first introduced to *T Nation* readers in 2004.

I've received thousands of email messages and forum questions about Tabata. Most of these fall into the "I wonder" category.

"Dan, I wonder if I can do it seven days a week?"

People who ask questions like that need to be thrown into the water. If they ask that question, it's clear they've never actually tried Tabata!

Tabata Refresher

For clarity, let's revisit what Japanese researcher Izumi Tabata said. His epic line was: "Six to eight very hard twenty-second intervals with ten-second rest periods may be one of the best possible training protocols."

A Tabata workout looks like this:

Work for 20 seconds
Rest for 10
Work for 20 seconds
Rest for 10
Work for 20 seconds
Rest for 10

Repeat five more times. The whole thing only takes four minutes, but those will be the longest four minutes of your life!

The Experiments Begin

I first read about the Tabata protocol during a time in my life when all I had was an Olympic bar, two thirty-five-pound plates and two twenty-five-pound plates. With a total of 165 pounds and an eagerness to compete at the national level as an Olympic lifter, I had to think things through a bit.

First I tried the Tabata protocol with weights. My journals record a number of epic failures. I tried more things and discovered I could bring on my own near-death experience with ninety-five pounds in the front squat if I could get sixteen to twenty reps for the first two minutes or so (per twenty seconds) and still nail eight or nine in the last twenty seconds.

I tried it with military presses and learned that the mass of the "pushing muscles" couldn't handle the amount of work.

When I first wrote about Tabata, I suggested doing thrusters, an odd front-squat-to-press variation. That was wrong. You should never put weight overhead in a fatigued state. Don't black out with the bar overhead. It can damage the floor.

Soon, I discovered one and only one weightlifting move that worked: the beloved front squat. Just keep your fingers on the bar during those delightful ten seconds of rest and keep going.

I strive for a weight that still allows around eight reps for the last set. That can be amazingly light, but you'll soon learn not to judge the workout by the first set of fourteen to twenty reps. The accumulation of fatigue will shock you.

Four New Ways to Tabata

Since I wrote my first article on this protocol, I've had the opportunity to try some "easier" variations that still work very well. The front squat remains the king of Tabata exercises, but here are a few twists:

1. Stationary Bike

The stationary bike, used by Tabata and therefore not a bad idea, is really well-suited for this job.

I remember doing this a few years ago and a colleague said, "This seems like just a warmup." Cranking out twenty seconds with as much load as I could crank, letting momentum spin my legs for ten, and holding on to this for four minutes was more than just a warmup. I stayed hot and sweaty for hours.

If excess post-exercise oxygen consumption (EPOC) is as effective as they say, this workout is its poster child. I felt like my own little space heater.

This variation is "easier" than front squats, but still a wonderful training addition.

2. Swings

This variation only works if you know how to do swings correctly.

If you feel swings in your lower back, you're doing them wrong and you need to stop. If swings make your hamstrings sing and feel smoked the next day, you're doing them right and you may continue.

3. Goblet Squat

For goblets, you can do the ten-second rests while cradling the 'bell in the standing position, or you can "rest" at the bottom in the deep-squat position. The latter would require a solid bottom position. Not everyone has that, so experiment here.

4. Farmer Walk

The farmer walk Tabata might be the safest of all the moves, but it does have a downside: grip. If you can hold it, I can guarantee you can keep walking.

The same guidelines apply: walk for twenty seconds, rest for ten, repeat six to eight times. You'll probably need a partner to call out the times for you.

At twenty seconds, set the weights down and try to breathe. At about eight seconds into the ten-second rest period, you should be re-gripping and getting ready to go again.

And Now, a Couple of Dumb Ideas

1. Tabata for Biceps

I was recently told there's a "Tabata Biceps Program."

Just shut up. I don't want to hear it. Tabata isn't about pumping up a small area of the body. It's about four minutes of honestly coming close to the end of your energy resources.

It doesn't burn fat in those four minutes; it burns fat in the next bunch of hours. It's not a workout to fill a muscle full of blood; it's a battle.

2. Sprinting

Also, I don't want to hear about sprinting variations. You can't sprint for twenty seconds and "suddenly" rest for ten. It doesn't work.

Someone mentioned a treadmill variation where you leap off and put your feet on the sides. Reminds me of the fisherman years ago who caught a baby rattlesnake and brought it close to his face to get a better look. (Rest in peace.)

Jumping on and off a treadmill sure sounds like a good idea... until you're tired.

Wrap-up

Through trial and error, use and misuse, the Tabata method has come full circle. The protocols above, from front squats to farmer walks, are your best tools for this method.

Is Tabata the hardest workout you'll ever do?

I wonder.

Four Challenges to Light Your Fire!

"Kick the tires and light the fires, big daddy!"

~ CAPTAIN WILDER, *INDEPENDENCE DAY*

Challenge One: Kick the PUPP

It's true, some coaches don't like the plank exercise. They say it's too easy, at least for their advanced athletes.

But here's the deal: If you start shaking like a wet cat in winter before you even reach the sixty-second mark, you need planks.

I know, I know, you're too advanced, just like everyone else on the internet, all of them just one cycle away from being Mr. Universe...but if you can't plank for one full minute, let's just pretend you need some work on this.

If you're the Olympic 400-meter champion, you can skip it. Fair enough?

Okay, so what's a plank? Basically, it's holding a pushup in the top position. Yes, it's that simple. I'd make you a video of it, but it would be quite boring.

Form? Well, a plank is like that Trex deck that will be straight 10,000 years after the end of the world. Make one smooth, straight line, hips solid, head locked in the military fashion, and body rigid. No need to coat yourself in deck varnish, though.

Planks are probably my favorite underrated exercise in my quiver of training tools. I now have about a dozen variations with names that mean something to me and nothing to anyone else. I think it's important for a coach and athlete to share a vocabulary, but translating these to print or online is impossible. So, I won't comment on star planks, dead bugs, getup planks or—my favorite—resurrected dead bugs with a heartbeat.

Let me give you one to try. I'd like you to fall to the floor and give me a PUPP: a standard pushup-position plank. The shaking in your waist after thirty seconds is a sign that your body wants to discuss some issues with you.

I'm going to ask that you do it the way we use it here. I want you to use the PUPP as your rest period for the workout.

Yeah, you read that right.

Take a squat movement and use a weight you can get for ten reps. For this workout, however, halve those reps, doing sets of five. Instead of resting, you will PUPP.

Here's an example:

> *Front squat × 5 (with 10-rep weight)*
> *PUPP for 30 seconds*
> *Front squat × 5*
> *PUPP for 30 seconds*
> *Front squat × 5*
> *PUPP for 30 seconds*

Be careful on the last set, as the heaving of the chest makes handling the barbell a bit suspect. I strongly encourage you to rest for a little bit after this workout.

Yes, you can PUPP longer than thirty seconds. Yes, five reps with a weight you can front squat for ten is very light. And guess what? Neither will matter when you attempt to leap off the ground and front squat that last set.

How about this? Try it first, then decide if you want to ask me about longer PUPPs and more weight on the bar.

Challenge Two: the Big 55

The next little idea I use in training is "The Big 55." I had a smart kid from the weightroom once answer a question very quickly in a math class. The instructor asked, "What's the sum of 10 plus 9 plus 8 plus 7 plus 6 plus 5 plus 4 plus 3 plus 2 plus 1?"

My lifter answered, "55!"

The instructor was amazed he could add those numbers so quickly until the student told him the truth: "That's Coach John's favorite workout."

Here's how to do it. First, put two moves back to back. This is a twisted little workout:

> *Swings*
> *Goblet squats*

The workout: do ten swings, followed by ten goblet squats, then nine and nine, eight and eight, and—you know where this is heading!—go all the way to one and one. I don't recommend putting the weight down if you're doing this with the same kettlebell or dumbbell.

Enjoy.

Notes

The swing is simple. Maintain a nice back arch, sit back, keep your head up, stay braced at the bottom, and use a powerful hip snap on every rep. The 'bell shouldn't rise above your shoulders.

Think of a goblet squat as a front squat holding a dumbbell in front of your body at your chest. This allows for a "comfortable," natural and upright position.

Challenge Three: the Twenty-Three-Minute Man-Maker

Pick five exercises. Like these:

> *Squat*
> *Overhead press*
> *Deadlift (any variation, use thick bars if you*
> *have them)*
> *Pullup (preferred) or pulldown*
> *Ab wheel or ab roll-out using a bar or*
> *Swiss ball*

The chore is to do ten reps back to back of each of the five lifts, then start again doing nine, then eight, then seven…and, again, yep, you guessed it.

I have a tap-out rule that you have to finish in twenty-three minutes. I insist you use weights that are so light in the squat, press and deadlift that you're embarrassed to begin the workout.

If you follow my sage advice, you might be able to finish it.

Challenge Four: Tumble

One other area of training most people have completely ignored is tumbling.

Tumbling is part of bodybuilding's history. Tumbling was a key to "body culture" a hundred years ago, and it existed well into the Muscle Beach era. Franco Columbo was a gifted acrobat and could do amazing things with his total body strength.

I'm telling you this: if you want a workout that will gas you and leave you sweating and crying in a heap, go ahead and tumble. The following workout recently led a fairly good athlete to puke:

> *Five forward rolls*
> *Five right-shoulder rolls*
> *Five left-shoulder rolls*
> *Three cartwheels followed by three cart-*
> *wheels to the other side*
> *One set of bear crawls (about ten meters)*
> *Sprint to waste basket*

The bear crawl is a quadruped crawl. The knees don't touch the ground, just the hands and feet. The two basic variations are the bent-knee Spider Man or "military" version, and the straight-leg version.

I don't like my athletes to puke, but the level of intensity, both physical and mental, that it takes to tumble really ramps up the metabolism.

Furthermore, I don't push the tumbling repetitions. We take time to review technique and position and protection. But the workload seems insane compared to rotator cuff exercises on a BOSU ball.

Summary

"Accept the challenges so that you may feel the exhilaration of victory," said General Patton.

Well, you're going to feel something after one of these challenges. Let's hope the exhilaration of victory is part of it!

Another Six Challenge Workout Ideas

1. The Demon Deacon

Many of us were amazed years ago when Ethan Reeve, the outstanding strength coach at Wake Forest, posted workouts on popular internet forums. He'd post the workouts and one or two examples of the actual weights and reps recorded. The numbers were stunning, and it reminded many of us that we just weren't born to be elite football players.

One workout became a staple of all my programs. It's simply this:

One rep on the minute, every minute, for the allotted time.

The time can vary from twenty minutes to an hour, but the key is the proper selection of load. It works best with the big lifts like the clean, power clean, front squat, and deadlift. The back squat doesn't seem to work well, as it seems one can always do another back squat.

For loading, try a lift that allows for a solid plate selection. For instance, two forty-five-pound plates on the ends of a bar (225 pounds) will work better than a whole bunch of assorted clanking plates.

The Demon Deacon works best if you do it with a partner. Some suggestions:

> *Front squat with 205*
> *Deadlift with 315*
> *Clean (or power clean) with 205*

If you want an interesting variation, try it with military presses. Use a "natural" number like 95, 115, or 135. Remember, it's a single rep on the minute, every minute, for the total time planned.

Certainly, you could plan on continuing to failure, but try your hand at twenty or thirty minutes first before extending to a full sixty-minute game.

The great benefit of this workout is focusing on a single movement and gathering your resources to make the lift over and over again. Obviously, I love this kind of thing.

2. The Bengal

When I first ventured into the internet, we could read discussions on open forums with NFL strength coaches and other legends of lifting. Unfortunately, the trolls literally drove them off and it still saddens me. Zit-faced fourteen-year-olds from the Midwest would say all kinds of terrible things, protected by the anonymity of the computer screen.

Before that happened, though, I remember Kim Wood, the strength coach of the Cincinnati Bengals during their Super Bowl years, discussing the hundred-rep challenge. I loved it, and it remains a staple of my challenges to this day.

It's very simple: Pick a lift, load it up appropriately, and do one hundred reps with it. I've done it using the following:

- 165 in the squat snatch
- 205 in the power clean
- 185 in the clean and jerk
- 255 in the front squat

For the sake of clarity, it's not ten sets of ten or whatever; it's 100 singles.

The idea is to pick a load that's challenging and continue doing it over and over. The workout can last over an hour and you might find you have minutes filled with multiple reps, interspersed with five-minute periods of pure rest.

Each time I do this workout, I come away with a better appreciation of the setup involved for each and every lift. It's actually a teaching session for experienced lifters.

One added benefit: you'll become an expert at math as you begin to think at, for example, twenty reps, that you're one-fifth there—which is twenty percent. And that means you have eighty to go…which is four-fifths. It's fun and educational!

3. The Eagle

You read about this one earlier. It combines the simplest of the loaded carries—the farmer walk—with the double-kettlebell front squat.

The person does eight double-kettlebell front squats and then drops the weight to the sides and does a farmer walk for twenty meters, then does another eight squats. We repeat until completing eight circuits and then hurl in a bush because the workload is incredible. The suggested load for a high school boy is two twenty-four-kilo 'bells while girls should start with twelve-kilo 'bells.

While the suggested load may seem light, oftentimes the goal wasn't met.

There are some hidden benefits to this combo. The person uses two kettlebells and never puts them down. The metabolic hit is accelerated by the grip work, the wrestling with the kettlebells, and the sheer volume of carrying the load.

There's nothing magical in the choice of exercises, it's just the patterning movement of loaded carries mixed with the grinding movement of squats.

4. The Spartan

I lived in Murray, Utah, and our local high school mascot was the Spartan, hence the name of this random workout. This is a workout for two people, and it's based on the classic "I go/you go" template. I'll give you two variations, but the theme is the same: a lot of movement with very simple tools.

Option One: Bear/Bear

- I recommend gloves for both partners.
- A duffle bag filled with up to three water-softener salt bags. Generally, each one weighs about forty pounds, so try to get two or three bags in the carrying sack. Duct tape it well.

Partner one does bear crawls while partner two carries the bag "bear hug" style. Stay in communication and switch well before fatigue sets in. Continue until…finished.

Option Two: Deadlift/Bear Crawl

Agree on a deadlift load, ideally using big plates to 225 or 315. Partner one deadlifts for five reps while partner two does bear crawls. Switch. Try this for five rounds the first time around. On the last set, do bear crawls to "failure."

5. The Coyote

This workout was a staple of the Coyote Point Kettlebell Club. It takes only one kettlebell per person and can be adjusted with reps, sets and load to fit anyone. Don't let the simplicity fool you.

- *15 Swings*
- *5 Goblet squats*
- *3 Pushups (or variations)*

That little workout covers all the basic human movements and has the odd ability to always allow "one more round." Try this for five rounds the first time and you'll find, by itself, an appropriate, repeatable, all-around workout. If you can handle the volume, twenty rounds equal 300 swings, 100 squats and 60 pushups, and is a respectable workout.

To make it harder, first increase the number of pushups. Then, add a bigger 'bell. This is a great workout anywhere, anytime and for any reason.

6. The Road Warrior

This is a workout I designed for members of one of our federal agencies who travel all the time and never know what equipment will be available. It's simple on paper but keeps conditioning "in the ballpark" until they come home again.

Day One

With dumbbell in one hand ONLY (let's say the left hand):

Before We Go

- *Waiter walk (short walk with weight overhead like a waiter)*
- *Suitcase carry (short walk with weight like a suitcase)*
- *Suitcase deadlifts*
- *One-hand overhead presses*
- *One-hand bench presses (keep other hand "free")*
- *Side bends*

Reps and sets depend on the weight available (and the energy available!). Get going and feel good.

Day Two

Do the same workout as day one, but with the right hand!

Day Three

Combine pushups and swings (or any variation)
- *5 Pushups*
- *20 Swings*
- *4 Pushups*
- *20 Swings*
- *3 Pushups*
- *20 Swings*
- *2 Pushups*
- *20 Swings*
- *1 Pushup*
- *20 Swings*

Repeat or adjust as appropriate.

Nine Tips for Dedicated Lifters

I STARTED LIFTING IN 1965. I've been employed as a strength coach since 1979. I've seen a lot come and go, but I'm fairly confident the following nine tips will still be around fifty years from now.

1. Do High-Rep Squats

Oh, I see the nonsense all the time. Instead of just lifting the bar, lift it for two seconds and then stretch it out to four and then slowly bring the weight down using an eight count. If you can do all that, you just aren't lifting enough.

High-rep back squats have been the mass-builder's secret before, during and, hopefully after the anabolic age. They work.

- If you weigh 135 pounds or below, use 135 when squatting.
- 135–185—use 185.
- 185–205—use 205.
- Everybody over 205 pounds—use 225.

When you squat deep for fifty reps, you'll understand the value of high-rep squats. After you do that, come back in two or three days and repeat it.

2. Carry Really Heavy Loads

This generation of lifters is lucky. They've seen the Strongman and Highland Games competitions, and most of them know about the farmer walk and the family of loaded carries, but the main issue hasn't changed in a decade: load.

I wrote an article years ago about farmer's carries, and the magazine showed a fitness model (male) carrying twin twenty-five-pound dumbbells. Those weren't farmer walks. Those were "salesman at Nordstrom's carrying out boxes of high-heeled shoes" walks. You need a bit more. Try using a trap bar with the same loads listed in tip number one. Strive for a hundred yards.

And if your grip gives out, don't turn and say, "My grip gave out." I have this idea that the body protects you by letting the weight drop. Over time the grip won't give out so soon.

3. Don't Get Fat

Working on fat loss sucks. It always has and it always will. I've lost fat through extreme diets and a liver parasite. Honestly, I don't know which was worse.

Art De Vany answered a question at a workshop once in a way that upset a lot of people in the audience. The question was, "What's the best thing for fat loss?" De Vany's answer was, "Don't get fat in the first place."

This advice still holds. There's a period in many people's lives where they just put things to the side for a few years and eat pizza and drink beer. If it took a decade to add all that blubber, try not to think you can burn it off in a week. It will include diet. It will include exercise. It will be harder than you think.

So don't get fat in the first place.

4. Stop What You're Doing for a While

If you've "tried everything" to reach a goal, try this: stop. For fat loss, go on a full week vacation at one of those inclusion resorts. Eat. Drink. Play. Sleep.

When you come back, step on the scale. Often, people lose weight on these vacations. Why? I don't know. I think it has to do with the whole "play and sleep" formula, but I could be wrong.

Once, while training to throw the discus, I got hit in the head by one. Yes, I took one across the skull. It would have killed a lesser human.

As a result of having a metal dinner plate crease my skull, my next year in the discus was the best I ever had. After seven years of never missing a day, a workout or a competition, I had to stop. I stopped lifting. I stopped training. Six months later, in October, I began training again and had the best season of my life. I crushed all of my personal records and was amazed to see the progress on a program that was literally half of what I used to do.

Sometimes, the path to a goal is a short retirement.

5. Don't Do Junk Conditioning

The longer I coach, the less I believe in conditioning. Look, when I was in high school, the Army came out with a series of booklets called *Conditioning for a Purpose*, but I think we sometimes forget the purpose.

In the discus, after my right foot comes up, I release the discus in one point six seconds. Two seconds would be the high end of my range for conditioning. Making a thrower jog might be a good idea, but it might also get us away from the goal of throwing farther.

Oh, I get it. We're in the age of YouTube, where people will load videos of themselves doing burpees so the world can see them.

Seriously, at elite levels, people still get tired playing basketball and soccer. It's normal. Playing two downs in a row for an NFL defensive lineman is exhausting. You can get that guy down to 220 pounds, but being in "better shape" isn't necessarily going to enable him to get to the quarterback.

Whenever you add some conditioning to your training, ask yourself if you're just spinning your wheels or pulling on the rower, as the case may be. Conditioning has value, no question about it, but if you're doing a bunch of junk for no rhyme or reason, cut it back or cut it out.

It's okay to be tired in victory.

6. See the Whole Picture

Make sure you know the whole story. Following a movie star's training program is almost always suspect. If you don't have a chef, a full-time assistant, an on-site personal trainer and the ability to get some of those "supplements" that can land most ordinary people in jail, you might have to change a few things.

Whenever I see a program with eight meals a day and three or more hours of daily training, I tend to just move along. Nothin' to see here, folks.

I generally make most of my meals, and I can't imagine the workload in preparing eight. I think that's why I really enjoyed moving in the direction of a kind of intermittent fasting—I'm just too lazy to prepare all the meals.

I've come to two conclusions about the best and brightest in sports: genes and geography. When standing around NBA guys, you get a sense of the need for height. If you were born and raised in Canada with an instinct for aggression, you might be a great hockey player. That same set of genes transferred to Iowa produces a wrestler, while similar traits produce an Olympic lifter in Bulgaria. It takes both genes and geography to be the best.

When you see extraordinary things, take a moment to look at the whole picture. Then, get your ass in gear and get back to work.

7. Shut Up about Inconsequential Stuff

Lifting weights is the following:

- Picking weights off the ground.
- Lifting weights overhead.
- Carrying weights for time or distance.

We can argue about the fundamental human movements, and I can once again answer questions about why I don't have "rotation work" in my weightroom, but if you won't do the three things listed above, shut up.

Yes, deadlifts, overhead presses and farmer walks are really that important. And yes, squats and pullups are good, but if you can't pull double-bodyweight off the ground, press bodyweight overhead and carry bodyweight for about a hundred yards, let's see if we can take care of that first, shall we?

8. Stop Wasting Time in the Gym

I'm thinking we should hook kitchen timers around people's necks and have them go off every five minutes. The way I see it, time in training is like a sandbag with a hole in it. Once you walk in the gym, your sandbag begins losing sand. Twenty minutes of foam rolling probably has value, but time spent rolling around is leaving you with an emptier bag. I don't care if static stretching is good or bad, but every minute you do of it is leaving sand on the floor.

We see it all the time: the extended warmup on a piece of cardio equipment followed by foam rolling, lacrosse ball rolling for "hot spots," fancy shoulder movements and the whole lot of stretches, twists and turns. By the time that person is ready to actually pull some weights, it's time to go.

The moment you enter the gym, the clock is ticking. That's why I like to have people squat first. If you have to leave, at least you got something done. The tradition in the O lifts is to do the big moves first, then do the "accessories."

Stop wasting time in the gym. Do all that rolling when you watch TV. Keep it out of the weightroom.

9. Stick with the Program

The best pre-workout supplement? Easy. It's the workout you did before today. Every workout should build, in some way, upon the previous session. If you keep leaping from idiotic program to idiotic program, you might never learn this lesson.

Nervous Energy and Peaking

Not long ago after a workshop I gave, I received this email:

> *According to an old graphic that belonged to Charlie*
> *Francis, here are some breakdowns when it comes to*
> *nervous system involvement on exercises:*
>
> > *Explosive work—90%*
> > *Lower body work—70% to 40%*
> > *Upper body work—40% to 25%*
> > *Isolation work—25% and lower*

One of my key pillars of training athletes is that there is a nervous system hit from training. Some things impact performance more than others, and that chart seems to capture it very well.

We find this in the weightroom with max deadlift work. After a true max deadlift, everything seems to sink for a few weeks. A session of goofing around with heavy deadlifts to win a bet my senior year in college almost cost me my discus season. I ended up with a hamstring pull when sprinting a few days later (the heavy deadlift made my hip feel "twitchy" and I compensated), and I struggled to recover for weeks.

When I was training with Dick Notmeyer, I couldn't do anything besides the Olympic lifts in training because, honestly, we didn't have time. The O lifts demand a massive amount of rest time between reps.

I have fond memories of Eric Seubert and me watching our sweat pool on the cement floor between sets. I often wondered how I was going to get back on the platform and do another rep!

That's the kind of hit we get from explosive work. You literally can't do heavy O lifts or heavy deadlifts and bounce back a few minutes later to have all the skills you need for exacting technical work.

There are several points that leap out here.

1. Francis's insight about these percents give us a clue about why "the biggest bang for the buck" programs tend to be shorter and sweeter.

That old training program of:

Day One

Bench press
Deadlift

Day Two

Bench press
Squat

...is a wonderful template for anyone too busy to train. But these workouts can be exhausting when looked at through Charlie's great insight.

I'm doing the Hercules Barbell Club Beginner's Program again, and I am fully behind Dave Turner's insistence that we only do it three days a week. I am sore in places I didn't know I had! Twenty-six total sets of O lifts in a workout is taxing.

2. This will also hint at why people who follow Frankenstein training—bodypart splits, isolation exercise (you know…traditional bodybuilding)—can spend so much time in the gym. I'm not saying this is bad, but when I watch people do four or five variations of curls, it's clear this isn't going to burn the nervous system up like a max clean and jerk. Writers from the last century used to call this "muscle spinning," and it's a route to hypertrophy, but I have yet to see it carry over into the athletic field. This isn't a "good or bad" statement, since many people have the goal of just looking better.

The reason this discussion is so important is that I often laugh when people ask me about peaking programs. If peaking was such a science, why don't we see everyone running, throwing and jumping personal records at the Olympic Trials?

Now, it might be hard to peak again at the Olympics a few months later, but, honestly, if peaking works, shouldn't everybody know that on the second Tuesday of June at 10:00 am, we need the ultimate performance? Why even host the trials, as we all know the top three are going to go on?

Guess what? It doesn't happen! Francis's insight also gives us a clue that the actual training to prep for a peak might be undoing the work. Please do NOT think I am recommending that you just do arm curls or whatever to save your nervous energy, but you can see what an art form it is to balance everything.

I will include my standard list of "peaking secrets."

1. First, realize you are powerless not to do something stupid. So, accept that. Embrace it. Now, promise yourself the following: the Goal is to keep the Goal the Goal.

Anything you add to your plan that's not part of the goal is the problem. Don't do it.

2. Pieces of paper are cheaper than surgeries. Write out your goals, a specific date to achieve them and a general plan from what has worked in the past and what has worked for others. This is ninety-nine percent of success in planning.

3. Grab a calendar and make a few big red Xs on dates when you know things are coming up. Now, don't be surprised when things come up. Next, take a yellow highlighter and highlight the days with "issues." It could be something as simple as school finals or appointments for the dog.

4. Steal other people's paths. We have tons of information available for anything you are attempting. Success leaves tracks: follow them.

5. Assemble the tools, supplies and information needed for correctives. If you are going to use a foam roller in this program, get a foam roller. Allow about ten percent of your training time to be restorative work, correctives and any kind of voodoo you think helps.

6. If you're involved in a sport, eighty percent of your training time should be doing that activity. For most, ten percent of your time should be on developing strength, another ten on correctives, but the bulk should be on the specific activity.

7. For most situations, the day before competition should be an eighty-percent day (hard to define, but most people

have a feel for that), but TWO days before should be sixty percent, perhaps just a warmup. The "Two-Day Lag Rule" has survived the test of time. If the event is really important, completely rest three days before and perhaps four days before, if possible. Don't try to stuff weeks, months or years of work in that last week.

8. The airline industry was made safer because of checklists. Use this formula for success: make checklists and follow them. If you need a list for your warmup or mobility work or whatever, make one. I'm reminded of the football team that showed up to a game without footballs. I remember that because I was the head coach. Use lists to free up space in your brain to focus on the work at hand.

9. Evaluate any program or system every two weeks. Make small course corrections when you're still basically on target.

10. Be sure (!!!) to plan something for the successful completion of the program, season or system. Look "after" the finish line, so to speak. Answer "Now what?" long before you come to that point.

I find this list of ten to be as helpful in storing nervous energy as any fancy, computerized printout.

Working Out on the Road

ONE OF MY RECENT FAVORITE movies is George Clooney's *Up in the Air*. Like many road warriors, I enjoyed the movie, but I honestly took a few notes too. I'm typically traveling every weekend, and I have my GO-Global, TSA pre-check, Diamond Status and mileage perks all inside my single carryon suitcase that I can live out of for seventeen days.

I wear underwear I wash in a sink, I carry extra instant coffee (there's rarely enough in the hotel room and a fresh pot costs as much as lunch), and I can layer myself warm in the coldest towns in Canada.

But, my health and fitness tend to suffer.

For those of you who travel and want to stay in shape, let's walk through a few ideas you can do anywhere and everywhere.

First, if you can do these three things, you can feel better:

1. Be sure to walk EVERY day somehow and somewhere.
2. Stretch your hip flexors, hamstrings, biceps and pecs daily.
3. Drink a lot of water, especially after waking, flying, driving and breathing.

The travel industry is conspiring to crush you into a little ball; fight back with those three tips.

For training, keep it simple!

Master the basics: the pushup is not only a great upper body exercise, but it also works the abdominal area better than anything we see on television in the late-hour infomercials.

Squatting, even just with a suitcase held to the chest, can be valuable for mobility, fat loss and a youthful rear end.

So, a workout can be this simple: pushups and goblet squats.

And, by the way, alternate these. Standing up from the pushup will drive your heart rate up and keep it there.

Now for a specific routine. Try "working down" the chain like this:

> *Do 10 pushups*
> *Do 10 goblet squats*
> *Do 9 pushups*
> *Do 9 goblet squats*
> *Do 8 pushups*
> *Do 8 goblet squats*

And so on, until you do one repetition of each exercise. That's fifty-five pushups and fifty-five squats, and a lot of getting up and down. It's fast and furious and works well.

If the hotel has a gym, it will probably underwhelm you. Recently, I trained in a hotel gym with a very expensive kettle-bell (I was told this by the manager) that weighed twenty-five pounds. It was half to a quarter of the size I would use in a typical workout.

Given the lightness of the weights, if they have dumbbells at all, consider this asymmetrical workout.

Day One

With a dumbbell only in your left hand, do:

1. *Waiter walk (short walk around with the weight straight over your head like a waiter)*

2. *Suitcase carry (short walk around with the weight held like you would a suitcase)*

3. *Suitcase deadlifts (holding the weight like you would a suitcase, do a deadlift)*

4. *One-hand overhead presses*

5. *One-hand bench presses (keep other hand free)*

6. *Side bends*

Day Two

Do the Day One workout, but with the weight in your right hand.

The reps and sets depend on the weight available (and the energy—travelling saps energy fast!). Just get it going and feel good.

The reason I do this is simple: I often have some energy on the first day of a trip. By the second or third day, I am ground down. So, I know all I need to do is finish the rest of my body—the other side—when I go into the gym. It is oddly easy to convince yourself before the Manager's Reception and happy hour to sneak in this quick workout.

These are just a few ideas. I know people who don't travel often will argue for much more, but the true road warriors will understand it. Sometimes doing any workout on the road trumps the vision of perfect training.

I always look forward to coming home and training hard.

Kettlebell Swing Mistakes

AT AROUND THE SAME TIME I started training in the '60s, the Nautilus machine and the Universal weight station pushed kettlebells, fixed barbells and gymnastics equipment from gym floors across the country. Disappearing with them was one of the best fat-burning exercises of all time: the swing.

While European and Australian coaches continued to use the move in their training programs, it took more than thirty years for the swing to make a resurgence in America.

Nowadays, 10,000-swing challenges are staged where Nautilus machines once stood.

Sadly, the swing is easy to screw up. And with the rising popularity of the kettlebell, this is more apparent than ever before. I watch YouTube videos of men picking up heavy 'bells and tossing them haphazardly in front of their bodies. I've seen trainers with horrendous form pass on their technique to clients. It makes me cringe.

Here are the ten most common mistakes I see, and the best ways to fix them. Swing away.

You Squat

This is the most common error I see. For some reason, people want to "sit" when the 'bell goes between their knees. But the swing is not a squat; it's a hip hinge.

The difference? During a squat, the hips and knees maximally bend. During a hip hinge, the hips maximally bend and the knees minimally bend.

Hinging at the hips until the torso is almost parallel to the floor allows you to engage the hamstrings, those large muscles that let you powerfully swing the kettlebell back up to the top. Bending the knees won't let you do that.

Your Lower Back Hurts

After a swing workout, your hamstrings should be sore. But if your lower back is bothering you instead, the problem is probably your hinge.

Some hinging pointers: guide the kettlebell toward your groin as it falls. (I know that sounds scary, but trust me.) As it nears the zipper area, bend at the hips and reach your arms back like you're deep-snapping to a punter. This keeps your back in a neutral position and effectively engages the hamstrings.

You Don't Plank

Think of the swing as two distinct movements: the hip hinge and the vertical plank. I've already cued how to hinge, but the plank at the top of the swing is equally important.

You want to be a straight line from your head to your feet. Pull your shoulders away from your ears, squeeze your glutes and quads, brace your abs and push your feet through the floor. Pretend as if the top of your head is stretching straight to Zenith.

It should look like you're performing a plank on the ground, but you're standing.

Your Eyes Wander

When you look up or look down, it throws the form out of alignment. Keep your eyes on the horizon, and continue to look at that point throughout the entire move.

You Lack Control

The kettlebell is heavy, and you need to generate a large amount of power to manage the weight. If you don't control it, it will control you—and that leads to injury.

Here's how to put some serious power behind the swing: After you hinge, forcefully explode your hips forward like you're performing a football tackle. Pretend as if you're throwing the weight in front of you. (Just think it. Don't actually release it!) As you hinge back, toss the weight toward your zipper. Do this every rep.

You Get Fancy

Although single-arm swings are great for cardio and increasing grip strength, the uneven load can cause you to sway or twist. Unless you have a kettlebell instructor taking you through the basics of a single-arm swing, stick with the standard two-handed version. It hasn't failed me yet.

Your Arms Go above Your Head

At the top of the swing, the kettlebell should end somewhere between belt and shoulder height. You'll know it's high enough when you feel the 'bell float—it goes weightless for a second. The heavier the 'bell, the lower the peak of the swing.

You Only Concentrate on the Swing

The start and finish of the swing deserve just as much respect as the move itself.

The better your setup, the better your first swing will be, so don't just throw the 'bell back without first getting into the proper stance. Before every set, I make sure my feet are gripping the floor, my hips are hinged back, my back is flat, my lats are engaged, my hands are creating torque by trying to break the kettlebell handle, and my eyes are on the horizon.

When finishing, don't just dump the 'bell on the floor. Instead, guide it gracefully to the floor in front of you. This shows mastery and means you're in control of the weight the entire time.

You're Still Struggling

No article or video can take the place of hands-on coaching. If you really want to learn how to master the swing, train with a certified kettlebell instructor. Quality instructors can offer regressions and corrections based on your background and challenges.

The Metabolic Swing

The Unknown Movement Pattern

To develop the idea we started earlier in the swing instruction, I'm going to tell you about the single most powerful movement pattern you can perform. Sadly, most people have no concept of how to do it.

It's the hinge.

What's the hinge? It's a basic human body movement few athletes and bodybuilders bother to train. It's the tackle and the check in hockey. It's that dynamic hip snap involved in the kettlebell swing, the snatch and the clean. It's also the vertical jump and the standing long jump.

It's not a squatty, slow move, but rather a dynamic snap. The truth is, the hinge, in its own right, is more powerful than the squat.

The Explosive Snap

The hinge is simply achieved by pushing the butt back.

Think about it: your upper body isn't sitting on top of your legs like a shack on stilts. Rather your body is "slung" between the legs.

Here's the issue: at first most people excessively bend the knees. But we need minimal knee bend in the hinge. Here's the formula:

> Squat: *Maximal knee bend and maximal hip bend*
>
> Hinge: *Minimal knee bend and maximal hip bend*

The benefits of a powerful hinge?

- Just learning to do the move correctly can open up hamstring flexibility.
- Doing it slowly with a massive load will impress your friends for generations.
- Learning to have symmetry in the movement can jump-start an injury-free career.
- Doing it fast? It's a one-stop shop to fat loss, power and improved athletic ability!

Swings: a Metabolic Hit

Swings are the top of the food chain of hinge movements. They're also the most underappreciated exercise in life, sport and most gyms. In fact, if all I could do for an athlete is teach a proper swing and encourage some form of deadlift, I'd be making a huge impact.

The metabolic hit of a correct set of swings is shocking. It's one of the best conditioning exercises I know. And according to a new study coming out of the University of Wisconsin, the kettlebell snatch, which is quite similar metabolically speaking, is "equivalent to running a six-minute mile pace" and "burns as many calories as cross-country skiing uphill at a fast pace."

So what's the best way to perform a swing? First, pattern, then grind and finally, swing!

Patterning: The Wall Drill

Patterning—learning and ingraining the hinge movement correctly—is important. That might sound odd because the hinge is such a natural human movement. But, when load is added, many people cheat themselves by not pushing the butt back, and instead trying to use the quads as the focus.

First we pattern using the wall drill.

1. Stand next to a wall, facing away. Hinge so your butt touches the wall. Step about six inches from the wall and repeat the butt touch.

2. Now move an inch or two more away and repeat. Keep doing this: touch the wall and scoot out a little more.

When you feel your hamstrings burning and shaking, you have it right. Like a bow and arrow, those strings can deliver an unbelievable amount of power.

Grinding

After patterning, we work on grinding. Grinding moves are slow strength moves that can work wonders for patterning while delivering a lot of metabolic work and improving strength.

Using either a heavy sandbag, a kettlebell or a weight plate, hug the weight to your chest, keeping the weight over your sternum and upper abs. Think of the waiter's bow exercise, only with the weight held a little lower.

Now, repeat the hinge movement.

I usually do a set of five, then repeat the wall drill.

Before We Go

This movement, which I call the Bulgarian goat bag swing, is an excellent way to slow down the hinge and teach the keys to more dynamic work: pressurized breathing, the correct feeling of the hip swing and the abdominal tightness that insures stability.

Symmetry

Before I move on to the million-dollar move, I always take a few minutes to check symmetry.

I use a mirror and a single kettlebell. Hold the 'bell in one hand and practice the hinge feeling. If you have to re-pattern the hinge with the wall drill and some Bulgarian goat belly swings, that's fine.

I look for the "CSZ" line. That's the "chin, sternum and zipper" line: all three should remain in a single vertical line.

Holding a kettlebell in one hand like you would a suitcase, do several hinges. I'm a big fan of single-arm moves, but this one really helps tie down the opposite side. If you feel yourself pulling "off-line," re-pattern the first two drills.

The Perfect Swing

If I had to pick one move that will burn fat, loosen the hips and legs and raise the buttocks to an eye-pleasing height, it would be the swing.

The swing can be taught horrifically. One TV expert came out with a DVD on kettlebells, and the swing technique was immoral. The swing is a simple move to watch, but a little more complex to learn.

Michael Perry, a certified kettlebell instructor, offers an excellent summary, which I'll borrow from below.

Start with a symmetrical stance and bend the knees slightly. This knee bend shouldn't change much throughout the movement.

302

Find the crease at your hips, put your hands in that crease, stick your butt behind you, and feel your hands fall into the crease. Make sure your spine is neutral while sticking your butt back. Breathe in and fill your diaphragm. This is the bottom of the swing.

Place your forearms on your inner thighs, at the top of the quad with straight arms. Push your arms into your legs and envision yourself holding two sheets of paper underneath your armpits. Keep your armpits tight and your arms close to the ribcage. This is how to stay connected at the bottom of the swing.

Bring your hips forward quickly, keep the arms tight to the ribcage, but allow the kettlebell to float to the three or nine o'clock position. Snap your hips and clench your glutes while shortening the distance from your ribcage to your pelvis. This is how you brace at the top of the swing.

Exhale but stay tight at the top of the swing. Keep your hands on the kettlebell to control it, but don't hold on too tight.

I also like the gas pedal and brake analogy.

1. *Hip-snap and pop the glutes = gas pedal*
2. *Tighten the lats and brace the abdomen = brakes*

Make sure you don't use too much gas or too much braking; balance them out to make the drive nice.

Okay, ready for some sore glutes and hammies? Here are some favorite workouts using the swing.

The X-Swings-Per-Day Method

Set a rep goal. It might be as little as seventy-five swings performed three days per week.

I made a goal of 250 swings a day in January, and at the end of it people asked me about my diet. My diet was awful and I ate and drank too much. But I started looking pretty good from the 250 swings. Yes, swings work that well.

One route is to come up with a number: seventy-five swings is excellent for beginners. Break it into bite-size sets like twenty or twenty-five.

I Go/You Go

If it's true that we need to teach our hearts to climb up and recover quickly (waving the heart rate), well, here's my contribution. This is my best swing workout.

The rep scheme is 5-10-15-15-10-5. Get a partner and alternate sets. That's sixty reps, and the rest period is only a few seconds between sets. Although you can do this up to five rounds, try one or two first before you make plans.

30/30

Another rep scheme, 30/30, also works well. Thirty seconds of swings, followed by thirty seconds of rest is a marvelous way to get a lot of work into a short period of time.

If all you have is ten minutes, try 30/30. Toss in a set of farmer walks and you've taken care of business.

As Good as It Gets

The hip-hinge is as good as it gets for the human body in terms of performance. Take the time to learn the basics and make this a big gun in your training arsenal.

How I Really Train

T NATION EDITOR-IN-CHIEF TC Luoma emailed me recently to ask about my ongoing evolution in strength training and conditioning. He essentially wanted to know how I train. You know, like for real.

I had no idea how to answer.

Everyone knows I first started lifting in 1965. I've competed in a host of strength sports and continue to be marveled and amazed that there's been so much progress and, indeed, so little.

Some people read my work and conclude there's nothing new under the sun. Actually, there's a ray of truth to that (sun...ray... get it?) as the basic benefits of the barbell are unchanged. But there are marvelous new inventions and rediscoveries that make training today, as I approach my first IHOP meal with a ten-percent discount on the senior's menu, as exciting as it was when I was fifteen.

Five Truths of the Idiot

The answer to the question, "How do you train?" is always evolving. For me, though, there are several "truths." (Now, I have to be careful, because I might change these truths next week.)

Truth One: I'm an idiot.

Truth Two: The key to proper training is to do what you need to do, not what you want to do.

Truth Three: If you're ignoring a basic human movement, well, that's the weakness in your program.

Truth Four: You need to be sure your loads and reps match.

Truth Five: The roles of some things are simply to refresh and recharge.

Truth One: I'm an idiot.

Happily, I know this. So, I hired a trainer, Buddy Walker, and I chose him because he has the strange ability to make me do things I don't want to do.

It's been said that any lawyer who represents himself has an idiot for a client. The same is true with programming in strength and athletics.

I'm Dan John and I'm an idiot.

I've tried repeatedly to coach myself. Here's what I do when I work in a typical gym setting.

Bench press
Incline press
Decline press
One-arm press
Military press

As you can see, I'm really good at pressing! So good, in fact, that when I was in high school, kids from other schools would come to South City to watch me bench.

Sadly, pressing is the last thing I need. Here's where my trainer, Buddy, comes in.

Buddy: "Dan. Do these Y-pulls on the TRX."

Me: "Why pull? Why not?" (I crack myself up.)

Buddy: "Yeah, funny. Ten more reps."

Buddy makes me do those things Perry Mason would make me cry about if I were on the witness stand: "Yes, yes. That's right. I need to do more rows, pulls, planks, that geeky lunge thing, and that other thing I hate. I admit it."

Now, if you don't have a personal trainer or a coach, you can sidestep this a little in a training community.

One thing I pride myself in is establishing training groups. In some groups, we gathered once a week and hit a general workout; now our group meets every morning.

Optimally, I'd suggest one meeting with a trainer each week, and at least one gathering a week. Both of these options force us to work the areas we'd rather ignore.

Truth Two: The key to proper training is to do what you need to do, not what you want to do.

One can easily see the connections between points one and two. What I usually want to do is the stuff I'm really good at. What I need to do is all of this:

Joint mobility, especially my hips and ankles
Vertical pulling
Thoracic mobility
Left-arm work
Balance drills

And I never do any of it. That brings us back to Truth One!

The reason I assess so much with my athletes is that I'm trying to illuminate their issues. We do it all: FMS, Bottle Cap tests, strength tests, my *Can You Go?* Assessments, and any other profiles I can get my hands on. I'm striving to have as many "You see? Here!" moments as I can before we start moving into…

Truth Three: If you are ignoring a basic human movement, well, that's the weakness in your program.

I make my living telling people to do goblet squats and farmer walks because almost no athlete who comes to me has either done these or done these correctly. Either way, the impact is immediate.

In my own training, I go out of my way to literally check off this list each week. It's funny to note how often I skip loaded carries, as this is what I always preach to my athletes. (See Truth One.)

I also believe in training a lot on the ground, especially as we age. I find myself doing lots of Turkish getups and rolls and rocks and cross-crawls on the ground to get that work in. As I often note, if all you did for a workout was get to the ground, get back up and repeat, well, that's a pretty exhausting workout.

Truth Four: You need to be sure your loads and reps match.

This is the key to extending a lifting career across decades. The key rep scheme is nearly universally fifteen to twenty-five reps. Yes, you can do the million-rep march, but you won't repeat that workout.

Certainly, for swings and the like, you can slide up to hundreds of reps, but usually you'll find fifteen to twenty-five is repeatable. If you can do lots and lots more, perhaps consider that your load is too light. You can't do fifteen? Perhaps, the load is too heavy.

The traditional programs represent this idea. Reg Park's famous 5 × 5 is the classic for building bulk and power. We also recognize 5 × 3, 3 × 5, 3 × 8, and the various programs that run up to this number, like 5-4-3-2-1.

There is a famous variation of this that has been used by many:

1 × 10 with 50% 10RM
1 × 5 with 75% 10RM
1 × 10 with 100% 10RM

In my training, repeatable workouts are the key. If the total reps start sliding up, I increase the load. I don't put a lot of emphasis on one particular set because my experience has taught me that I have this great ability to blow up big lifts out of nowhere.

I look for the total as my guide.

Truth Five: The roles of some things are simply to refresh and recharge.

I recently bought the coolest bicycle ever—a Panama Jack Cruiser. It has a beer holder, coaster brakes and only one gear. Basically, it's a bottle opener with a bike attached. I use it to do cardio or fat burning or whatever we call it now. It's inefficient, slow and hard to bang up a hill. All this makes it better for fat loss than your cool little racer and your shaved legs.

Much of our training time should be things that refresh and recharge us. I love spending time on bike rides with my wife, when we'll stop and talk and laugh and spend hours riding along the trails. We don't check our pulses or get GPS updates. We ride. We refresh.

That's the missing element of most people's training. Any idiot can get you tired (sure, do 10,000 jumping jacks), but to continue to make progress and keep on keeping on, you can't always race.

My Actual Training

So what do I honestly do? Generally, Sundays are easy days for bike riding or walking. As for the rest of the week:

Monday

- Turkish getups.
- Alternating clean and press with a single kettlebell. I keep the weights light and use this as a warming movement.
- TRX Rip trainer moves for hips and mobility.
- Double-kettlebell presses—usually ladders, 2-3-5-10-2-3-5-10 or 2-3-5-2-3-5.

Tuesday—Session with Personal Trainer

- All kinds of mobility mixed with specific body area strengthening (usually on a TRX).
- Ab wheels, bench press, pullups and Aerodyne in a complex.
- More stuff I hate.

Wednesday—Group Training

- Lots of goblet squats, swings and loaded carries.

Thursday

Usually this is a day off, but that would still include swimming, biking or running. In earlier days, a group of us went to the beach and did a little kettlebell work, followed by a dip in the northern Pacific Ocean. In the San Francisco Bay Area, the water is c-o-l-d!

Friday

Usually, this is the day I work on more pressing, but I get some focused workouts on the kettlebell snatch for high reps to keep my groove.

Saturday

Often I'm give a workshop on the weekends. If not, I sit with my journal and note the gaps. This tends to be a day for some waiter walks, extra pull work and some combinations of swings, goblet squats and pushups.

Bonus: Sleep

I'm as sick as the next person over this new fear of doing anything without three hours of mobility complexes, foam rolling and tissue work. The recovery area I'm most impressed with relates to the king of recovery: sleep.

So, before I end any discussion of "How does Danny train?" let's talk about sleep. Ever since Robb Wolf recommended the book *Lights Out,* I've taken sleep more seriously.

I once dropped from 226 to 213 in a week on my way to getting down to 209 pounds for an Olympic lifting meet by trying to sleep twelve hours a day. I was amazed when it worked. Not long before this, though, I had two friends both tell me they couldn't sleep through the night any more.

Within a year—

One left his wife for what I'd consider a "poor choice."

The other left his wife for what I'd consider a "poor choice."

I began to notice that men start complaining about lack of sleep just before that mid-life crisis. I decided not to go there. I take sleep hygiene seriously.

Good bed.

Good shades.

Quiet room.

Comfortable temperature.

Don't watch TV or surf the net about half an hour before going to bed.

Nothing earthshaking so far.

Robb insists on Vitamin D before sleep. He recommends the liquid kind and I take one drop with 5,000 IUs. I don't know the difference between pills and liquid, but I trust the experts. Then, I start shoveling down the following from Biotest:

- Z-12. I don't think this should be used in excess, but that's true of anything.
- ZMA. There's an argument that we should increase this to six capsules to help with testosterone levels, but I don't always have the opportunity to sprint to a toilet in the morning. Also, I love ZMA dreams!
- Alpha Male, for the aforementioned T levels.

Then, there's fish oil. I take a lot of fish oil. I try to constantly sneak up the amount I take too. With a quality fish oil, I don't need to take as many to get what I'm looking for.

I believe the hype about fish oil—I see it in my athletes and I see it in myself. It not only gives an edge in performance, but it seems to help with skin health. Remember, the skin is the largest organ of the body. If the skin looks better, something good should be going on inside, too.

A final point: Steve Ledbetter has me experimenting with an anti-inflammation trick concerning travel. I fly out nearly every Friday and come back Sunday or Monday. Every week, I deal with the TSA types, the nervous, sweating rookie flier on one side of me, and the person who doesn't understand that farting in a plane is poor travel etiquette. I also deal with my legs swelling up so my socks bind my ankles.

He's got me cutting down on grains, increasing veggies and fish, drinking more water and trying to double my fish oil and

ZMA when feasible. None of this is a recommendation; this is merely what I'm doing for a specific issue.

But it's worthy of consideration and something I want you to think about: How can you proactively keep ahead of your career, school or life demands and stay on your path to your goals? This is just one way I approach this issue.

I work on recovery in a number of different ways beyond this, too, but sleep is the key. I own a mechanized massage table and probably a dozen things like rollers, balls and odd knobby things for tissue health. It's all good, but not as good as quality sleep.

Summing Up

So that is how I train and restore my body.

As for the food side of the equation—and that's an important one—for me it's almost universally meat (eggs, fish, chicken…and bacon!) and veggies.

I try to drink excessive amounts of water, but I notice the more I stick to just meat and veggies, the better I feel overall. I make a daily goal of trying to eat at least ten to fourteen different kinds of veggies. It's fun to try this and it makes shopping and dining out an adventure. You'll find onions, green peppers, tomatoes and olives are in nearly everything now, but expand your options a little.

Focusing on covering all the human movements, sleep and striving to eat a variety of vegetables is a pretty simple formula for lifetime health. The important thing is, I use daily, weekly and monthly checks to monitor that I'm not getting too far off course.

And on my birthday in August, I will be ordering a side of veggies with my senior's meal.

The Five Key Principles for Fitness Professionals

IT'S A RARE WORKSHOP that I don't start with goals and goal setting. It's also a rare day when I don't ask the basic questions of "What is your goal?" and "Where are you on the road to this goal?"

The flipside of goal setting is ongoing assessment. I usually point out that Point B is the goal and the big question is what is Point A—literally, where are you now?

This requires ongoing assessment, and whether it's my assessments from *Can You Go?*, the FMS, strength tests, blood tests, body composition tests, flexibility tests or timed drills, these give us an idea of where we are today.

The first day I did the Olympic lifts, Dick Notmeyer told me that the bare minimum for a lifter was a bodyweight snatch. At my first meet three weeks later, I did that, and Jim Schmitz told me that very soon I would snatch what I clean and jerked (231) that day.

And I did it in nine months. This history lesson reminds us that clear standards are an efficient tool for guiding us from here to there.

What Keeps You Going?

I'm a big fan of resolutions and goal setting, but what keeps us coming back? One of the keys to my success as a coach, I believe, has been my ability to see that ongoing adherence to goal setting seems to need three additional points:

Results
Don't make me look stupid!
Community

When I talk about results at a workshop, I have to hold back the urge to say "obviously." Yet results are often overlooked in fitness and health discussions. Spend five minutes on the various chest-pumping sites on the internet. There have been wars with less macho posturing than some people's discussions about their chosen combination of squats and pushups.

We see numbers, times, unwatchable videos and all kinds of avatars with various warriors from *300* or some other blood-lust film. But when I go to a gathering and meet these same internet warriors, it's often hard to tell if any of them lift weights or even train in some manner.

Training comes down to results. It's so obvious, it's hard to type the words. That's why I love the sports that have made my career, throwing and lifting. If we add this or that to our training and I throw farther or lift more, whatever we did was right.

So, here's my question to you:

How Do You Measure Results?

If you're here to impress the ladies (to look good nekkid, as an email stated), are you actually impressing the ladies? I'd suggest better hygiene, better dancing ability or learning how to talk without sounding like a total fool would help most guys more than a six-pack. (For some of you, yes, having her drink a six-pack will make you look better.)

For body comp goals, where are your before-and-after pics, your measurements, and your fat-loss measurements? Don't guess, do! That's the key here.

If you want to be a Navy SEAL, have you joined the Navy? If you want to be in the NFL, are you playing for a team now?

It's that clear in my head. Beyond that, are you getting results?

If you're making a living in the fitness industry, your clients are your best advertising. That's why before and after pictures are so important for selling your skills.

John Berardi, Josh Hillis and many others have made the use of these pictures mainstream, but it really is a radical idea—here's where I am, and this is where I was. If I'm making progress, things are working.

I use results to test programs and programming. After a review of my journal, which I've kept since 1971, I realized the two best programs I ever did for pure strength and preparedness for throwing consisted of only two workouts a week.

The next key to ongoing progress is something I missed for a long time: "Don't make me look stupid."

Putting a fourteen-year-old girl in the varsity football weight-lifting class will make her look stupid. As hard as she tries, she'll always stand out in the class because of her gender and the obvious need to lighten the load.

Making an overweight mother of three do something very public that she fails at isn't going to keep her coming back for more.

This is why I constantly discuss the need for mastery of movements and a certain amount of grace in training. You know it when you see it, like a great baseball player moving towards a ball. (I suggest reading the fiction work *The Art of Fielding* by Chad Harbach for some really interesting insights on this topic.)

When I coach mastery of movement, I actively work against the problem of "Don't make me look stupid."

This doesn't mean I don't challenge the athlete, the middle-age woman or the fourteen-year-old girl. Certainly, I do. But with proper coaching cues, enough repetitions, and appropriate regressions and progressions of movement, everyone can look masterful while training.

Ignoring this, in my experience, kills progress, and the person quits and moves on to something else.

This is why I believe in the "Killer App" approach to using equipment. There's a great show about how the computer went from being something only NASA would use to literally being my sole form of work and entertainment.

It came down to a simple thing: spreadsheets. An accountant saw this and said, "I hire 200 people to do this forty hours a week and you're telling me I only have to push one button?"

That's a killer app.

For the kettlebell, it's the swing, the goblet squat and the getup. The TRX and various rings give us the horizontal pull, the one-arm pull and the various T, Y and Is for the upper back.

For the barbell, it's the deadlift and all varieties of the press.

Mastery of this list will give athletes all they need from the weightroom, and any person the body of their dreams. Mastery walks hand in hand with simplicity.

The third quality that supports goal achievement is appropriate community.

Whenever I advise a new gym owner, I talk about safety, cleanliness and a vision of training that will keep people coming back. Then, I talk about community outreach, from canned food drives to pushups for charity and anything else that will get the name of the gym out to the public in a positive way.

But there's also the need for internal community too.

One of my best memories of coaching is taking two hurdlers and fourteen throwers to a track meet. I'd just finished reading a book that emphasized that rich people cheer on the success of other rich people. It struck me that this is a tool we used at Skyline College and Utah State on our teams.

"Team" is the key here, and many may have forgotten that some of us were trained to put country, church, team and family ahead of our own needs and desires.

My idea was to encourage the kids to madly cheer for each other to get personal records. It was magic—not only did we take the first six places in the girls' discus throw, but every athlete scored lifetime bests that day. I treated the team to a fast-food banquet, and that memory is among the top five memories I have of my teaching and coaching career.

It's easy to recruit to a team after an event like that—my athletes became the best ambassadors I could ask for after the meet. Building excellence also breeds an interest in more excellence.

I've often told visitors to my facilities that the key to building an outstanding program is that we need to empower our athletes and clients to become our assistant coaches. There's no higher calling than to teach, and when you explain something to someone else, the winner tends to be you as the clarity comes through.

I like training alone, but a training partner or my team, the Hercules Barbell Club, always brings the best out of me. I've made lifts in meets simply to not let down my team. Community can bring out the best in us.

Goal setting is crucial. It's the base of the training template. Goal setting gives us a chance to clear away the clutter and focus on "this," whatever the goal is.

Ongoing assessment is often forgotten. The old standby joke, "When you're up to your ass in alligators, it's nice to remember why you drained the swamp," is always useful in assessment.

Let's put all this together into some key principles to make you better at your craft.

The Five Key Principles for Coaches and Trainers (and Gym Rats)

1. Your athletes' and clients' goals are the most important.

Yes, we all know that this personal trainer is the former Mr. Greater Midvale and that skinny PT over there used to be a ballet dancer and a gymnast. That's great. Your people want to lose fat, feel better and improve the quality of their lives. Focus on that. Put your client's goals first during any training session and professional time.

2. Your athletes and clients, overall, want results.

Yes, there are other things, but no matter how fun, fantastical, stimulating and wonderful your gym setup has become, people, over time, want results. If you have a lean and mean setup with boring music, but your clients are the talk of the town because of their results, you'll be extremely successful.

3. Your athletes and clients don't want to look stupid.

Some of the best instruction in gyms historically is from other gym members. There's a tradition of helping the new people with the movements and equipment. If, however, you decide to constantly change the movements and workouts so it's always "Day One" for everyone, your people will feel like they look stupid.

Mastery is a lost art in the fitness industry, but people crave mastering movements and improving efficiency. If you have the courage to do a lot of repetition, your facility will be full.

4. Your athletes and clients want community.

There are dozens of excellent DVDs on the market, yet people come to train in a facility. It's part of human nature. We all know we can train harder when the people around us are moving. We also seem to enjoy donating time, energy, food and clothing to help others, and having a fitness component to a charitable drive seems to make it a win-win for everyone. Foster community and the community will foster you.

5. Your athletes and clients are your best press agents.

You can blind us with dazzling ads in all kinds of media. You can post, print and package all kinds of materials that will make us feel we need to open our wallet and send you money.

That rarely lasts long. Your clients are your "truth." Every time a client refers a person to you, be sure to step back and see what you did right. In fact, ask. Then, repeat what you did.

Go Forth and Prosper

Most fitness pros have probably established personal, business and fitness goals to make the most of the upcoming year. However, don't forget about your clients, and how you can successfully guide them along the journey from Point A to Point B.

Forty Years of Insight

I HAVE A BOX IN MY STORAGE ROOM that contains all my training journals. Besides sets and reps, I toss in what's going on in my life. Often, I find long essays about the future, lists about what worked, and funny little tidbits about my life I would've quickly forgotten had I not written them down.

It hit me when I picked up this box the other day that I've been recording workouts since 1971, five years after first picking up a weight. That's forty-five years! I started to think about the lessons I've learned and, before I knew it, I had a list of forty lessons I had to learn the hard way.

Lesson One: Keep a journal of some kind.

It makes me smile to see my attempt at neat handwriting in my first journal entries. The bench press workout was 85 × 8/8/4. I noted, "I was supposed to do six on the second set, but it was too easy." In the summer before my freshman year, I benched one hundred pounds; my sophomore year, I benched 200 pounds; and I got 300 during my junior year during track season. I would write what I benched as a senior weighing 162 pounds, but you wouldn't believe it.

I have a few notes about my coach's son who came to our weightroom one afternoon to see if I was "really as strong as my dad said I was." I told him I'd already lifted and he said something that questioned my lifts. So, I put a low 300-pound lift on the bar and it went up so fast that he told me to stop. "I believe you... wow, I believe you."

The value of a journal is seeing the progress (and the regress) of your training and training philosophy. I believe a thorough review of old journals is probably as good as a training session.

Lesson Two: Eat like a man.

An article Chris Shugart wrote pulled together some wonderful disconnected links that had spun in my brain for a few years. The article was called *Eat Like a Man,* and it featured five days of zero- or low-carb eating and two feast days. Yes, low carb is good, but carbs are not evil. For the strength enthusiast, or anyone who wants to just be powerful, this article gave the template. The carb-depletion workout fit perfectly with a weekly volume day. The carb-up fit perfectly with life.

Now, you can agree or disagree with the diet, but all the athletes I had use this template found that their ability to train longer and harder was naturally enhanced by this eating program. And, as the author notes, people fear you in the supermarket!

Lesson Three: You must master the squat movement.

You may not need to ever squat heavy, and you may also discover there are some better tools for you (*for you,* read that part carefully) like Bulgarian split-squats or pistols, but mastery of the squat is worth every second you spend on it.

Over the years I've written templates to follow. However, I still feel that the message hasn't been delivered: *You must master this basic movement.*

Spend years on it if you have to, as I did, but learn to do it well.

Lesson Four: There are several modern classics that will support your training goals.

Yes, these are books, but the depth and insights are important.

Cormac McCarthy's *The Road*
This one still stuns me and scares me.
(The diet advice is unsupported by research.)

T. H. White's *The Once and Future King*
The first part is *The Sword in the Stone,*
a book that changed my life.

Frank Herbert's *Dune*
The book is a science fiction legend, but the respect for
education, in all its forms, makes it worth reading.

I would also tell you to read all of *Harry Potter.* Any book that introduces a character in the first chapter that's so crucial to the whole story, yet won't be seen again until the third book, and a question from the very beginning that isn't answered until literally the end, deserves our time and energy.

There are others, of course, but the idea is that at times big goals and big stories also include epic tragedy and overcoming failure.

Lesson Five: Lift outdoors.

When I first made waves as a writer, I was usually quoted for insisting we go outside to train. It's still great advice. I still think carrying equipment outside and working out in a communal gathering is the single best way to train. As a discus thrower, bringing my kettlebell to the field to do a few movements "now and again" was a game changer in helping improve my throws. Grab some food and drink and a training tool, and go outside and have some fun lifting.

Lesson Six: The Southwood Program works.

I've written about this many times. You probably already know this one.

The Southwood Program is performed three days a week in the gym:

> *Power clean, 8-6-4*
> *Military press, 8-6-4*
> *Front squat, 8-6-4*
> *Bench press, 8-6-4*

Although I learned this while Nixon was president and nobody traded with China, it still holds fast as a great training program. You don't miss a single bodypart; it's simple to learn, and a bit rigorous to do. It also demands that you clean and military press, which we'll get back to later.

Lesson Seven: Learn to meditate or relax on command.

If there's a skill that's overlooked, it's the ability to nap when necessary. If my athletes struggle with getting or staying asleep, we're going to have issues down the line. Training oneself to relax is the first step. I recommend squeezing a muscle tight, then breathing out and releasing it. This helps enable falling effortlessly asleep literally anytime, anywhere.

Sleep is the best recovery tool I know, but the skill of sound sleeping is often overlooked. Although I recommend ZMA, eye-shades, and earplugs to just about every audience I speak to, I still say we also need to practice relaxing. There are many CDs, DVDs, and downloads that walk you through this skill. It's worth your time to practice this underrated skill.

Lesson Eight: Never pass a pullup bar without doing some pullups.

My all-time best number of pullups was fourteen when getting ready for my senior year of high school football. I know this because of my journal (see Lesson One!). As I grew larger, I let myself slide all the way down to four reps. I also noted that my shoulders hurt.

Then I started doing one or two pullups throughout my workouts. When two became ridiculously easy, I moved to three and soon to four. Once I got back to nine pullups, "miraculously" my shoulder health went back to being fine.

One surprising point about pullups is that they're also a wonderful abdominal exercise. I don't know why that is, but it will be evident the day after a long pullup workout.

Lesson Nine: The old-time weightlifters had it right— fixed weights are better for most of us.

I love pictures of old-time strongmen with huge kettlebells and fixed bars. When I first started training, gyms had fixed barbells in a rack, so we could grab a seventy-five-pound barbell or a 105-pounder, just like from a dumbbell rack today.

There's some beauty in this. Originally when I started with kettlebells, all I had was a fifty-three-pound kettlebell and a seventy-pounder. When I trained, I had two options. That lack of options made me dig down harder for certain movements.

A few years ago, I noted that most of us should toss out the bulk of our weightlifting plates and just use 45s and 25s. One would have thought I'd blasphemed! I got negative feedback for weeks from that.

I still stand by that. Yes, it's a jump to go from 185 to 225. It means you have to own 185, and you'd better be ready for the load at 225. It's also how we trained in college, because the small plates were all broken and the football team stole all the thirty-fives to stick on their machines (I won't comment).

My first group of recruits when I began coaching learned to lift with 95, 135 and 185 pounds in the snatch and clean. They mastered the loads quickly because, well, we had no other options!

Lesson Ten: I believe that for overall health, you need to help the body cleanse.

At nearly every talk I give, I note the importance of dental floss. Flossing is really good for us and it appears it makes a difference in heart health. It takes about a minute to do it. But I get emails from guys who tell me, "I'll do anything to get to X, Y or Z." When I ask them first to floss twice a day, I get a return email that says something like "that's a problem as…" Listen, if you don't have the discipline to floss twice a day, good luck with the Velocity Diet.

I do all the weird stuff. I use a Neti Pot for my sinuses, and I no longer need to take allergy medicine, so it "works." I use a tongue scraper every morning and learned that some foods really do make mucus. I always supplement with fiber. Now, I don't go so far as to do some of the higher-end stuff like colonics, but that's not a judgment on my part.

Taking a little time each day to "cleanse" is worth it to our overall health. To me, it's like eating vegetables and fruit. It's got to be good for us at some level. And, let's be honest, it's pretty easy to do.

Lesson Eleven: "90% of success is simply showing up."
~ Woody Allen

When I first began throwing the discus as a 118-pound tower of terror, I won a lot of meets. No matter what, the kids at the other school would say, "If (insert the name of a fat kid) would've been here, he would've beaten you." I used to believe that crap.

Whenever I win something, especially now in the internet age, I always find out later that "somebody else" would've won it if, of course, they'd just shown up. Folks, it's a truism that should be stuck to your bathroom mirror: "Show up!"

I have those memories of helping a friend off the floor as he was dieting down for an amateur bodybuilding contest and he was doing depleting workouts. He was in a brain fog for probably three weeks. Of course, on the dais under the lights, he looked magnificent and won "easily."

The dude showed up. If you're gunna gunna, you have to show up to prove it. "Gunna gunna" was a phrase my mom used for people who were "gunna do this and gunna do that."

It's like graduating from high school or college. I swear to you, if you just show up, you're gunna gunna do just fine.

Lesson Twelve: Safety must be part of performance.

Steve Ilg's *Total Body Transformation* has amazing insights into human performance and reflects on Ilg's courageous victory over a terrifying back injury. In the book, Ilg looks at a quote made about Mark Allen, that he had become the World's Greatest Athlete by winning a series of triathlons. Ilg came up with an interesting contest to see who actually was the world's fittest human.

Steve's contest included basic gymnastic movements, weight-lifting maxes and yoga moves. My favorite section was the third day's endurance event, a mountain bike race to an uphill finish. His genius is realizing that downhill is where the injuries happen, so why not test the athletes' fitness as safely as possible?

I've had a lot of injuries that have caused me to spend a lot of time in hospital beds. One thing I've learned is that it is "almost" okay to get injured in competition, but it's insane to get hurt in preparation.

Stopping several reps short of failure or injury may not sound courageous on paper, but coming back to train tomorrow is more important than an additional junk rep.

Lesson Thirteen: We tend to be glib about our weaknesses.

I love the word "glib." Usually, it means nonchalant (that has to be a French word; we need to find a way to say this glibly), but it also means "lacking depth and substance."

Now, most of my ex-girlfriends say that about me, but I digress.

I've always taken about six weeks a year to assess, reassess and deal with my weaknesses. It's always around the same few issues:

> *I'm too fat.*
> *My hamstrings are too tight.*
> *I need to work on X, Y or Z.*

How do I usually address these issues? Most people usually address weaknesses while also doing literally everything else. What happens in a typical six-week assessment program is that we continue doing everything we did before, and hope the weaknesses vanish magically. Without Harry Potter, that isn't going to happen.

In the last decade I've discovered that weaknesses demand full concentration. Weaknesses need to be given full attention.

If you have flexibility issues holding you back, you need some kind of challenge. In the past I've recommended the thirty-day yoga challenge (promise to go to ninety-minute sessions every day for thirty days), and I still can't think of a better way to address flexibility.

Weaknesses need to be attacked with depth. I charge you to examine every possibility in your search for ridding yourself of a weakness. I've had people squat five days a week to address poor squatting technique and do 1,000 full turns for a month to deal with discus throwing issues.

If you have a clear weakness, your plan has to be total focus with every tool and weapon you can muster.

Don't be glib.

Lesson Fourteen: Conditioning isn't just jogging.

Neither is it treadmilling, or whatever machine you're thinking of right now.

Conditioning is more than that. The intensity of conditioning trumps the duration most of the time. Most people don't train hard enough to get in and get out.

That said, I also think hiking, biking and long, easy treks along the beaches and meadows of this fine planet are underappreciated. As noted earlier, go outside and breathe real air.

Lesson Fifteen: It's the movements you're NOT doing that are impeding your progress.

I talk a lot about the five basic human movements. Now, you can certainly add vertical and horizontal and rotational and many other things to my list, but if you're skipping one of the basic five human movements, your training isn't optimal.

You're probably missing loaded carries and squats. One lesson I've learned over and over is that most people ignore those two things. Start doing farmer walks, waiter walks, suitcase walk, sleds and pushing cars a few days a week and master the basics of squatting.

You won't believe the progress you'll make.

Lesson Sixteen: There was a touch of brilliance in the Atkins Diet, and most people missed it.

I still love the Atkins Diet. I keep some correspondences from 1999 from a group of women who lost a hundred pounds each doing the Atkins Diet and a little weightlifting. I probably learned more from them than I ever learned from people with a bunch of initials after their names.

Here was the genius behind Atkins, in case you missed it. Dr. Atkins notes in his book that to become obese, you did something unbalanced. To get yourself back to sleek, lithe, firm and fantastic, you honestly can't do a balanced approach.

Finding balance at one hundred pounds over-fat will keep you there. He recommended an "unbalanced" approach to get back to your target.

I've used this contrarian thinking process ever since I read that. In coaching the throws, I teach athletes with bad habits to throw with the other hand, do things backwards, try throwing with the fifty-six-pound weight and a variety of things I'd consider unbalanced. Now, if I'm working with a raw beginner, obviously I'd pattern and model the best technique possible, but with someone with ingrained bad habits, I look for ways to completely rework the system.

If you've been training for four years and never really squatted, I'd recommend you squat five days a week for two years. Crazy? Yes! But that's exactly what Dick Notmeyer had me do, and not only did I add forty pounds of lean body mass in four months, I also mastered the movement.

This theme seems to be a reoccurring lesson in my career.

Lesson Seventeen: You can't do everything at once!

But if you do decide to do everything at once for a while, there may be benefits at the other end of the wormhole.

By the time I was a senior at Utah State University, I'd lifted at least three days a week, usually five to eight times, for nearly eight years. I played football, soccer, wrestled and competed at a fairly high level as an Olympic lifter. Oh, and I was a Division One thrower gathering points as a discus thrower, hammer thrower and shot putter.

In January of my senior year, I hit the wall. I was sick of lifting and just couldn't keep up with trying to do everything.

This "plan" worked perfectly. After all those years of training half the year as a thrower and the other half as an athlete in another sport, and keeping an enormous load in the weightroom, I backed off everything.

I never went over 385 in the squat that winter and spring. I did clean and snatch but always within reason. I didn't play in pick-up games or intramurals or, honestly, anything. I went to school, lifted a little and threw a little. I ended up with what Coach Maughan called "the greatest season in the history of USU throwing," which, at the time, was quite a big deal.

The lesson? Well, after doing seven years of "everything," backing off to just one thing propelled me to a level of success that amazed me with the ease with which I attained it.

Less is more. This is a fundamental truism in the strength arts.

But you first have to really put a lot of "more" in. Like Earl Nightingale used to say about the fireplace, many people walk up to the fireplace and say "give me heat." The right way to do it is to get some paper, some kindling, some logs and light a match. Then you get some heat.

You have to explore and learn and try many things to be able later to whittle them all down into a small package. I can show you some shortcuts and so can all the other coaches, but you need to put the time and effort into the "more" before you can master the "less."

Lesson Eighteen: You want less? Let me give you less.

I told you earlier about the King of Less Training Program. Here's your quick review:

Day One	Day Two
Bench press	*Bench press*
Squat	*Deadlift*

And then the tweaks:

> *Only 45- and 25-pound plates!*
>
> *No less than ten reps on every set of bench and squat until the last set.*
>
> *No less than five reps on every deadlift.*

That's it. It's the minimalist's minimal workout.

Lesson Nineteen: If you really want a breakthrough, teach someone else. And if you need mastery, teach sixty-five fourteen-year-old sophomore boys something all at once.

Whenever I talk with someone who has been around gyms for a long time, usually this story comes up:

"I was just a young kid and I wanted to lift. So, I signed up and tried to do what I thought was lifting. Some of the more experienced guys would take time to show me how to (fill in the blank) and, boy, did I make progress after that!"

The interesting thing is the experienced guys probably got more out of the exchange than the neophyte. When you try to teach something you know, you begin to pick up those subtle points you may have forgotten or, perhaps more common, you may know but never knew you knew it.

Teaching someone to squat might make you rethink how you move the whole system down, not just bending the knees.

Oh, sure, you can lose your mind helping someone learn the basics of weight training, but usually the time spent teaching others is like finding a vein of pure gold.

Lesson Twenty: When reading something over the top that has the markings of "secret" or "exotic" or even "expensive," don't leap in with both feet and break your ankles.

I've been there. I read those massive ads for Nautilus in *Scholastic Coach* and *Athletic Journal* and thought, for sure, that was the ticket to success. Plyometrics had me leaping off tall buildings with a single bound and limping up flights of stairs.

Don't even get me started with the stupid things I've tried.

Most of "it" is crap. From the magic supplements, like B-15 (better than fourteen!), to the promises of this huckster or that guru, I've rarely discovered much that works beyond the basics.

I remember fasting for fourteen hours before a workout and doing set after set after set of compound leg exercises and consuming a whiff of some exotic herbs to enhance my growth hormone. That enhanced someone else's wallet.

If it sounds too good to be true, it is.

Lesson Twenty-One: Put your money where your mouth is.

One thing that Laree, my publisher, finds interesting about me is that I sit in the front row at conferences. Each year I go to camps, clinic, workshops, conferences and gatherings. I buy nearly every new book and DVD on the market. I read and comment on a lot, although as a rule I only comment after I read something and only universally after I've tried it.

Now, this might seem counter to Lesson Twenty, but as the saying goes, an intelligent person can hold conflicting opinions in his head.

Here's the thing: I appreciate Mike Boyle's insights about single-leg training. Why? Because I've listened to him talk about it several times. I like his logic; I like his decision-making process. Moreover, I also like the long conversations we've had discussing it.

I strongly believe in spending money to get exposed to the cutting edge of what's going on in the field of strength and conditioning. I read and reread books, magazines, ebooks and blog posts, trying to cut away the extraneous and hone the message.

It costs me money to do this. And I'm okay with that.

Lesson Twenty-Two: You want to know about fat loss? Ask a competitive bodybuilder!

This is so obvious I'm embarrassed to write it. I've had the opportunity to sit with some fairly high-level bodybuilders and train with some of the best of all time. I can promise you the training tools of elite bodybuilders are the same weapons you use in the gym.

When it comes to diet, though, you need to listen up. There's this thing called "protein," and that seems like the only thing you need to think about when cutting fat. Carbs and even fat become misty islands far off in the distance that one may or may not see again for a while.

These guys are serious. My friend Lance once described his sodium loading cycle for an upcoming contest, and it was like sitting in the front row of a chemistry class, except I'd missed the first few months of the semester.

One of my coaching principles is that success leaves tracks. If you really want good advice about fat loss, talk to a competitive bodybuilder. Avoid the weekly magazine advice you see at the supermarket checkout and get some real information.

Lesson Twenty-Three: You may get another injury. But do you have another recovery?

This one is near and dear to my heart. I have an unbending training principle that's as old as medicine: "First, do no harm."

Any coach, program or training system that injures people is wrong. If you're an athlete in a sport that has an age or year ceiling (high school or college eligibility, for example) and you lose a year to an injury, you don't get that back.

My doctor said something interesting. If you're seventy-five and have a major joint repair, its purpose is to literally to help you go to the toilet on your own. At fifty-five, the same surgery might ensure a quality of life that will keep you young. At fifteen, this surgery is a tragedy for an athlete and one may never be able to compete at the higher levels of sport.

Recovery from injury or surgery may take tremendous resources to attain. Besides the financial toll, which can be overwhelming, there's a physical and emotional toll from injuries. I've been on crutches several times in my life, and there's not a single aspect of life that's easy on crutches. From bowel movements to escalators, every action and move has to be thought through before attempting it.

Sure, you can get injured, but you may not have another recovery in you.

In high school, my mom and sister could help out if I was hurt. When my daughters were little and I had wrist surgeries, I had to buy shoes without laces because when my wife wasn't around, no one was there to tie them!

Plan your training with intelligence and foresight. Train hard, but try to avoid things that can't be fixed without a surgical team.

Lesson Twenty-Four: Yes, intensity trumps everything. But...

There's no question that running hills or doing Tabata front squats is the "best way" to heat up your system, burn fat and make the world a safer place. However, I think we've lost sight of the importance of "easy," especially in the fat-loss race.

You can make a lot of progress on an interval training program. However, don't throw out the importance of long, easy cardio like walks or heavy hands. A long walk won't hit your fat stores like a furnace or whatever the ad copy says, but it will give your body a chance to recover and perhaps find some gentle, easy ways to lose the muffin top.

The principle here is to move away from "either/or" in strength and conditioning. My career has been built on the idea that "everything works, for a while" and while Tabatas and other interval training might be fun to watch, there's nothing sinful about a nice long walk. Moreover, like hiking, long walks tend to be more open ended, and rarely does one look at a watch worrying about "getting it all in."

Keep those tough high-intensity interval training (HIIT) workouts, the hill sprints and the hard stuff, but don't forget to add long lazy "workouts" as part of your palette.

Lesson Twenty-Five: Stop judging everything!

Train hard, but enjoy competition. Compete strenuously, but enjoy your training. One key point to keep in mind: never judge a workout or competition as "good" or "bad" solely on a single day.

I often tell new throwers, "Sorry, you just aren't good enough to be disappointed." Judging one's worth as an athlete over the results of a single day is just idiocy and will lead to long-term failure. Epictetus, the Roman Stoic philosopher, tells us, "We must ever bear in mind that apart from the will there is nothing good or bad, and that we must not try to anticipate or to direct events, but merely to accept them with intelligence."

Get in the gym and train. Finish your plan and shower. Then, be sure to come back to do what Woody Allen says: "Show up!"

Lesson Twenty-Six: Press weights over your head.

When I was in the ninth grade, one quarter of my training was the military press, and I made progress. Then I dropped it. My progress stalled. When I met Dick Notmeyer, literally everything was over my head, and I made progress again.

As I aged, I dropped the overhead stuff and everything went to my belly. I started up with one-arm kettlebell presses and my waistline shrunk back to a reasonable girth.

If Janda was right and certain muscles weaken with age (and he is, trust me), a quick study of that group should give you an idea of why you should press:

Rhomboids
Mid-back
Triceps
Gluteus maximus
Deep abs
External obliques
Deltoids

There's no question that one-arm overhead presses work the obliques better than all those odd side bends and twisties we see every day in the gym. Now, you might argue that the glutes don't work, but try to press anything over 100 pounds one-handed with a sleepy butt. I've tried it many times, and I think I may have done it once.

When in doubt, press overhead.

Lesson Twenty-Seven: For volume, do ladders.

I hate workouts like ten sets of ten. For one thing, I never remember what set I'm on. I know I'm supposed to use matches or cards or something to keep track, but I'm old and never remember those, either.

I like ladders. A ladder is a series of reps that usually go up. The first set is always easy, as the reps and load are low. The last set seems hard, but it's odd because you feel like you recover in an instant.

The standard ladders are:

1-2-3-1-2-3—you do a single, rest, a double, rest, a triple, rest, a single, ad infinitum!

1-2-3-4-5-1-2-3-4-5-1-2...

And my favorites:

2-3-5-2-3-5...

2-3-5-10-2-3-5-10-2-3...

I love 2-3-5-10 for hypertrophy. If you do that cluster five times, that's 100 quality reps, and you'll storm through the doubles and the triples with practically no rest. You'll finish strong and pumped.

2-3-5-2-3-5-2-3 is my favorite variation of the standard 5 × 5 protocol. Again, how quickly you get through the reps and the ease of adding more plates is a pleasant surprise.

I know of no easier way to add volume than with ladders.

Lesson Twenty-Eight: Last lift/best lift. Last throw/best throw.

These are mantras I repeat to myself and to my athletes. I've won national championships in lifting and throwing on the very last lift or throw. I do it with so much regularity that Don Bailey, a fellow thrower, has told people I do it on purpose for "the theater." It's not true, but I do like the point.

It always works well in training. Charlie Francis, the late, great sprint coach, ended workouts when his athletes got a personal record in anything. His idea was "there you go—you peaked—now rest."

That's an extreme, but I wish I would have known this when I was younger. Injuries tend to show up when you decide to add just a little more to your lifetime best. Learn to celebrate success and keep improving over the long haul.

This skill has to be practiced. You have to draw a line in the sand and say, "This is it. This is the last thing I do today, and it's going to be my best effort."

Now, I know most lifters don't do this, but I also know that most don't make any gains!

Always strive to leave practice and workouts "on top."

Lesson Twenty-Nine: Recharge.

This is a new idea for me. After a hard workout, come back the next day and, at a low level, move through the basic patterns of the human body in a kind of movement massage. The loads are light, the reps are unimportant, but the movement is key. For adults, I often recommend up to three of these easy recharge workouts a week. It can be as simple as doing the basic patterning movements.

Follow those with an easy walk. It doesn't have to be much, but you'll thank me as your mobility, flexibility and patterning improve without much residual soreness.

Lesson Thirty: The value of two.

Dick Notmeyer smiled and nodded as I told him about my weightlifting career. I thought I'd done it all. I had a big bench and could do pullups with the best of them.

Then he stopped me: "Here you're going to do snatches and clean and jerks."

That was basically it. For two years, I did the Olympic lifts in the summer sun and foggy blindness. It was rep after rep after rep.

And I made tremendous progress.

When Pavel came out with *Power to the People* where he suggested five days a week of deadlifts and side presses, a few brave souls took the challenge and expanded their work capacity. His Program Minimum of nothing but swings and getups is still my go-to recommendation for someone exploring the goals of general conditioning.

In *Beyond Bodybuilding,* he sets up a hypertrophy program consisting of five days a week of deadlifts and bench presses under the direction of DeLorme and Watkins, the founders of what we now call progressive resistance exercise.

I'm a fan of minimal workouts. The biggest reason is there's no wiggle room for "coulda, woulda, shoulda." The very essence of this training idea is "do this!" It's not the kind of training for someone who needs music, TV, internet and conversation during sets. Folks, it's dull work—actually, it's work.

Every so often, try two weeks of just two movements. Make the combination cover the bulk of the body and strive for mastery of the movements. It can change your training life.

Lesson Thirty-One: The stronger you are, the more you can get away with.

Josh Hillis notes that when women can do three pullups and deadlift or squat 135 for five, almost universally they're around nineteen percent bodyfat, which is what he calls Rockstar Hot. Since he told me that, I've been carefully watching the physiques of women, although to be honest I've been doing that since puberty.

There's another issue. Women who can do three pullups and show some numbers on the barbell can also go out after a clinic and have a good time.

Recently at a bar, a top female physique contestant told me that, "Oh, I can go out and party and not watch every single bite when I'm not peaking." Unlike the "skinny fat" women we see in the weekly magazines, this woman was strong enough that when she trained, her body had to gather up a lot of resources to adapt and recover.

What does this mean for you?

I've seen it many times at workshops and clinics. The skinny, weak guys bring their weighed chicken breasts and magic protein bars for the day. When we do something physical, they fade into the corn rows. The big, strong guys who have never seen a Strongman event will jump in and flail around dangerously close to death and dismemberment, but fight the good fight with the anvil, axle or stone.

Then they eat passionately and without apology.

In other words, as Brett Jones taught me, absolute strength is the glass. Everything else is the liquid that goes into the glass. The bigger the glass, the bigger everything else can be.

So get stronger and eat more without freaking out about it.

Lesson Thirty-Two: List your highs and lows.

Twice at the Olympic training center we were asked to take some time to do an "autobiography." Really, we just listed the best and worst of our athletic careers. We were allowed to add life events too.

I still have my lists. They're odd to look at from a decades-plus distance, but I still smile when I see "Turkey Day Football" and "Picked to Start for Brentwood" and "Winning hit in 1967" mixed in with performances that are worthy of national ranking. I don't want to address the "Worst" list, but that was the point.

After a fairly long wait for everyone to finish, we were asked to look at the lifetime lows.

"Put your finger on it," we were told. Now, look at the high side and see if there's a match.

"Huh?"

Just do it.

Incredibly, for the bulk of us every low "worst moment" lead directly to a best moment. Keep Lesson Twenty-Five in mind (don't judge everything), but the lesson that day was clear. Our lows are often the steppingstone to the greatest moments of our lives.

I've used this little exercise with my athletes and in my classrooms. Sadly, there are some who argue that they have very few "best" moments. It should come as no surprise that these timid souls often have no "worst" moments either.

Lesson Thirty-Three: Keeping the Little Red Book.

I have an extremely damaged tiny spiral notebook. It's red and falling apart. Since 1973, I've been keeping quotes in here that inspire me.

"The guy with the biggest butt lifts the biggest weights."
~ Paul Anderson

"Self-confidence, positive mental outlook and honest hard work."
~ Arnold's Three-Part Secret

"Greatness comes to those who dare to sweat,
dare to strain and dare the pain."
~ Dick Notmeyer

"Quality is the key, not quantity."
~ Bill Koch

"Never, never give up. Never give up."
~ Winston Churchill

"Yield to all and you soon have nothing left to yield."
~ Aesop

I also include training programs from people I admire and odd snips of ideas that still are forming in my head.

Here's one final one:

> "Do something different, something
> unique; make yourself stand apart."

I wrote that in my English class as a senior in high school to answer something along the lines of, "What do you want to be when you grow up?"

Lesson Thirty-Four: Follow the Leaders.

I was lucky to have the magazine *Strength and Health* growing up. It didn't just have bodybuilding information; that magazine really respected all areas of strength. Several times a year I could read about throwers or football players.

An article on a discus thrower named Gary Ordway came at a great time in my life as I'd embarked on an attempt to be a thrower. The article listed his workouts—I'll only note his top lifts in his preseason workout:

> *Squats: 505 × 3*
> *Deadlift: 455 × 3*
> *Power clean: 285 × 2*
> *Incline press: 325 × 3*
> *Situps: 4 sets of 25*

As a kid inclining under a hundred pounds, the direction was clear. I needed to get stronger. Now I knew the path—lift weights.

To be a strength athlete, you have to engage in a progressive program to lead you to your goals. The nice thing about lifting is the numbers are crystal clear. I'm benching ninety-five and you're benching 405. I have to get stronger!

This is why I still like the Olympic lifts and the deadlift for comparing generations. The O lifts and the deadlift have essentially stagnated for the past twenty years. Certainly there are amazing lifts, but there's been less than stellar improvement across the board.

Marty Gallagher loves to point out that outside of gear (in this case, squat suits, squat briefs, bench shirts, wraps and the like), there's been almost no progress in powerlifting. Yes, there are exceptions, but like O lifting, the sport has slowed to a crawl.

Discover what the best are doing. Look at what you're doing. Now shrink the gap.

Lesson Thirty-Five: If it improves a track and field athlete, I'm all ears.

This is a criticism that gets tossed in my face sometimes. I'm a snob, a prude if you will, when it comes to track and field. I love reading how this magic program, device or herb is the "do all and be all." Fine. Take your profits, invest in some athletes, and prove it at a track meet.

The response is always something along the lines of, "Well, this isn't sports specific," or, "Track depends on perfection of biomechanics."

Okay, fine.

It's easy to convince someone that a weight "feels lighter." It's not so easy to add three feet to the shot put or drop time off the 200-meter sprint.

If your idea works for sprinters, throwers and the rest of track and field, I'm going to sit in the front row and take notes. Even if I disagree with everything you say, if you get it right in track and field, and probably swimming, too, you're right and I'll listen to this grand scheme.

Lesson Thirty-Six: It's not "hydrating," it's drinking some damn water.

This looks like a rant, but, really, this drives me crazy. Moms show up to practice and ask, "Are the boys hydrating?" No, first perspiration, then hydration.

The area from your hips to your shoulders is now the "core." Today, Grandma asks if discus throwing "builds your core." Is shot putting "functional?"

To play a one-hour game of soccer—or twenty minutes of standing and forty minutes of picking daisies—my daughter used to get a sports drink, an orange, cookies and a treat. This was to counteract the incredible efforts of a group of seven-year-old girls who usually forgot which goal to kick the ball toward.

I'm tired of it. Let's bring an end to this pseudo-quasi-scientific language that's permeating youth sports, recreation and adult fitness. We're getting fatter at a rate no one predicted twenty years ago and yet parents flock around their kids like paparazzi around this week's latest Lindsay Lohan scandal.

It's called "water." Deal with it.

Lesson Thirty-Seven: You will wish you did it earlier than later.

I have an axiom when asked for advice. "Well, in four years, you're going to be four years older no matter what, but if you go to college, you'll have your degree." Or, "In thirty years, you're going to be thirty years older no matter what, but if you save ten percent of your income, you'll have a comfortable retirement."

The longer you put off something like squat mastery or eating clean, the more you'll regret it later. Now, I don't know when and what's going to happen, but life seems so much easier when you master the basics, make yourself a slave to good habits, save ten percent of your income and nurture quality relationships now versus later.

Get the degree, finish the thesis, buy good insurance, see your dentist twice a year and do all the boring things of life as often as you can. Trust me, your health—financial, physical, spiritual and emotional—will benefit from taking care of business early on.

Some of the athletes I first worked with are now sneaking up on age fifty, and two are already over the half-century mark. Whenever we talk, the most common gift that I bestowed on them was this understanding to get things done.

Lesson Thirty-Eight: Fat-loss exercise is about being as inefficient as you can be.

Aerobic dance continues to flourish in community centers. There's a lot of "woos" you hear when you walk past. What you don't see is progress. Now if I took the introductory class, I'd get the workout of a lifetime. Why? Because I would suck at it!

Fat-loss exercise, however, and it breaks my heart to say this, is about being completely inefficient.

Aerobic dance and most of the TV fitness devices work for a few weeks. Then, you get good at whatever it is and progress stops.

This is why I like the kettlebell swing for fat loss. It's a massive body move that eats up a ton of energy and you move nowhere. In fact, as you improve, you probably attack the movement harder, causing you to still move nowhere.

Len Schwartz's HeavyHands uses the same principle. You load up a couple of dumbbells in each hand and go for a walk.

With big pumping arm movements, you waste a ton of energy up and down and turn an easy walk in the park to an extremely wasteful use of energy.

And you burn fat.

I love the combination of swings and pushups or goblet squats and pushups for fat loss. The secret to fat loss is that wonderful pause after finishing the pushup when you have to get back up. It would be "better" to press, as that would save energy, but in this case, that's bad.

For fat-loss exercise, discover things you're terrible at and do them. If you've never skated before, pad up and see how a quarter-mile can ruin you for hours. As you get better technically, find something else!

It's the polar opposite of getting good at a sport or skill, but this is one reason why consistent fat loss is so elusive for most people.

Lesson Thirty-Nine: A workshop or a clinic is better than a workout.

I've argued for years that taking a weekend to listen and learn is far better than doing the "same old, same old" in workouts.

There's a need for all of us to humble ourselves and open up to new ideas. You probably should hang on to eighty percent of what you know, but be willing to throw out that other twenty percent and fill the space with something that will get you to the next level.

This sounds similar to "put your money where your mouth is," but there's more to this. The hotel bar after a workshop or the lunch between sessions or the hallway outside the conference is an opportunity to grow in ways we can only imagine.

You might get a chance to fill out a napkin (don't lose that napkin) with a training program from one of the great names in the iron game. You might get invited to a dinner or a party and meet people who will change your life.

You have to go to these events to understand the idea behind the ideas you see presented in this book.

Lesson Forty: In forty years, a lot of great people are going to pass over to the next existence.

It's a rare day I don't think of my mom and dad, Coach Maughan and some of my heroes and friends who are no longer alive. I carry on, as best I can, but it's becoming woefully obvious that my torch is burning dim, and I'll be passing it along sooner than later.

That's why I write. That's why I keep lists. That's why I answer the same questions over and over and over.

Our time on this precious Earth is short. Good health and a measure of strength can help us live a better quality of life.

And that's the greatest lesson of my life.

Before We Go

As we come to the close of a workshop, talk or lecture, I often add: "Before we go…" and, according to some, I make a point that has little to do with the material covered, but seems more important than anything I did cover.

It's often about where I'm heading with my career, or it can just be a concern. I often call upon the community to help out.

So, before we go, let me share with you our family motto.

Make a Difference.

When making a choice or decision, I run it through "Make a Difference."

The direction that will impact the most people in a positive way is where I strive to go. When it comes to sharing my time, my treasures and my talents, I always try to make a difference in a positive way to the most people.

So, before we go…

Make a Difference.

Appendix—Reading List

BOOKS SAVED MY LIFE. I had been in the Great Books program as a child, but none of them ever really had an impact on me. In the eighth grade (insert the standard joke: "the best three years of my life"), I found myself too small and too slow to play football.

And that had to change.

At the Orange Public Library, I found two books, T. H. White's *The Sword in the Stone* and Eliot Asinof's *Seven Days to Sunday*. The first book was about a young King Arthur and the second was about the New York Giants football team. These books piqued the left and right brain of a lonely pre-adolescent football player. Arthur learned from the animals how to be strong and defeat the enemy. *Seven Days to Sunday* is literally a day-by-day exploration of a week leading up to a pivotal game. On Wednesday, Asinof introduces us to the linebacker Ken Avery, whose life story became my template for training.

Books continue to change my life. One thing I strongly suggest is re-reading good books. I find that great books demand a second or third or fourth look. I believe it was Roger Ebert who taught that a classic is a movie you couldn't bear being told that you could never see again. I think the same about great books: one's life would be diminished by NOT having the chance to reread a book.

I enjoy books in which education is a major theme. Alexandre Dumas' epic *The Count of Monte Cristo* centers around Edmund's time learning within the Abbé's chamber. Yes, the treasure is marvelous and the slowly cooked revenge plot is delicious, but it's the classroom that changes our hero.

Frank Herbert's *Dune* is another book that gives continuing education a key role. It helps to learn desert power if you live in a waterless place.

Michael Crichton's two books *Jurassic Park* and *The Lost World* are more than just "how to make a dinosaur." The philosophical discussions, especially the question, "yes, we could, but should we?" still make for fabulous reading.

Recently, I reread the *Iliad* and *The Odyssey*. Christopher McDougall makes a good point in *Natural Born Heroes* that these two books are about hospitality. The first is a case study of when the guests ignore proper house rules and steal a wife. In the second, one of the great heroes of history who is well past his prime is asked far too many questions. A bit of good advice: don't trust all of Ulysses' stories after he was found naked near the princess.

Oh, and Ulysses wins the discus throw. He will always receive high marks from me for this feat. Reading Homer's classics highlights the role of hero in our lives (literally, "protector") and I argue that all of us are called to this.

For coaching, let me recommend a few books. Coaching is first and foremost economics. Michael Lewis' book *Moneyball* might be the best explanation of cost to benefit in the history of economic thought.

I wouldn't mind demanding that every coach read *The Richest Man in Babylon* by George Samuel Clason. It's available for free now, and the lessons are timeless: A part of all you earn is yours to keep. Good coaching is economics, but good coaches also need some money to survive.

I pulled one great thing from *The Millionaire Mind* by Thomas J. Stanley. The rich, when hearing that other millionaires got a windfall, are happy for them and cheer them along. Maybe we can use this insight for improving our physiques and performance: cheer for your opponents to do their absolute best and ride that success train to the top.

One of the first books I ever bought on strength training was *Body-Building and Self-Defense* by Myles Callum. This book hinted at the role that the fighting arts would have in the future of strength training. Not long after, Bruce Lee would discuss lifting and isometrics, and Arnold would discuss Lee's influence on him.

Ken Shamrock's book, *Enter the Lion's Den* reminded me about tumbling, and I added tumbling and self-defense work back into my training systems.

That was something I knew from the beginning!

Let me just add that at about that same time, I saw three books: a German book, Ulrich Jonath's *Circuit Training,* John Jessee's *Wrestling Physical Conditioning Encyclopedia* and an article about Percy Cerutty (later a book by Larry Myers, *Training with Cerutty*). Yes, I have read many wonderful and great books on strength and conditioning since 1971, but so much has been simply footnotes to these classics.

In other words, like so often in life, I knew the secrets from the beginning. "In the beginning"…that has a nice ring to it. Maybe I can start a book with it.

But, I digress, as usual.

The fundamentals, the basics, the simple path are always obvious and clear. They are the staples of success. Anyone who tells you differently is selling something.

It's the message of all the great books and all the great mentors, teachers and coaches.

Trust the basics.

For More from Dan—Wandering Weights: Our Epic Journey through All Things Heavy

SOMETIMES YOU MISS THE MOST interesting training-related articles. Sometimes the ideas in the most talked-about articles are confusing. You're not sure what to think.

Sometimes Dan just makes you laugh.

We've got you covered! Each Wednesday Dan gives us a short overview of what he's reading and what he's thinking about while he reads. All you have to do to get his free weekly review is to sign up.

And when you click the confirmation link, we'll send you a copy of Dan's five-page report called *The Quadrants of Diet and Exercise,* one of his most-discussed training concepts. Enter your email address at the link below to keep up with Dan's conversations.

http://danjohn.net/wandering-weights/

You Can Also Tap into the Brains of Some of the World's Leading Performance Experts

You can also sign up for free access to information from some of the world's leading performance experts through On Target Publications. You'll get the latest articles, interviews, specials and product release details sent straight to your email.

You'll also get FREE lifetime access to the OTP Vault, which contains articles and videos from experts like Dan John, Gray Cook, Stuart McGill, Lorimer Moseley and more.

To get your key to the OTP Vault, enter your name and email at the following link.

http://otpbooks.com/Dan-John-Book-Bonus

Index

Secrets about the Author

—Tiffini Hemingway John

In August 1987, Dan John was a high school history teacher who drove a rusted Volkswagen Super Beetle with its rear bumper held on by a weight belt. He had sworn off women and dating. He was convinced he would never get married nor have kids.

All that changed one week before his thirtieth birthday. Dan agreed to accompany one of his assistant coaches to a party, where the coach was being set up on a date with a girl named Tiffini Hemingway. That began a whirlwind relationship resulting in a wedding in May of 1988. His fear of never being a father was alleviated in 1990 and again in 1992 with the birth of his daughters.

Dan's favorite holiday is Thanksgiving. He's such a fan that he insists on "practicing" Thanksgiving at least four times a year.

He received an Irish tin whistle as a gift and practices it every day.

Finally, the man is a crier. He tears up when he's happy, and he tears up when he's sad. Whether he's watching the opening scene of *Love Actually,* or attempting to get through singing a verse of "Danny Boy" to his grandson Danny, you had better make sure there are tissues nearby.

Two of Dan's favorite sayings are: "It's not where you start, it's where you finish" (the John family motto), and "Make a difference."

Dan John is proof positive of both.